Original Prints III

Original Prints III

New Writing from Scottish Women

Polygon
EDINBURGH

© Individual Contributors
Introduction © Loretta Bresciani
Polygon
22 George Square, Edinburgh

Set in Linotron Sabon
by Alan Sutton Publishing, and
printed and bound in Great Britain by
Billing and Sons, Worcester

British Library Cataloguing
  in Publication Data
Original prints
Vol. 3 —
1. Short stories in English.
   Scottish women writers,
   1945 — Anthologies
   823'.01'089287 [FS]

ISBN 0 7486 6017 8

CONTENTS

FOREWORD

This is the third of Polygon's Original Prints collections. The first appeared in 1985. Then, as now, Scotland appeared to be enjoying something of a literary boom. What was apparent, however, and not only on Polygon's lists, was a lack of women emerging with their male counterparts. Historically, women have not been given the time, credibility or interest they need to take on writing seriously. This is as true today as it ever was — though the disadvantage may operate more covertly. Most established publishers — and especially Scottish publishers — have tended, by their prejudices, not to help much. Hence this series. It goes a little way to assuring that women may write with more confidence, having a place to publish. Work needs to be published in order that writers and readers both may develop critically.

This, then, is the anthology's function. Beyond simply publishing the work, there can be no definition or boundaries set as to what 'women's writing' is, should or can be. The most that can be said is that we are maybe in the business of producing a voice. The search for a voice is not a narrow pursuit. Voice is organic and constantly changing. It is always being remoulded and redefined. Being flexible, articulating experience, feeling, or whatever this voice may encourage, can prove by example that women need not be left out in the cold.

Many readers will find this collection 'uneven', which is to say, not all stories and poems match up with their expectations of such a voice. There were many arguments among the women who — with difficulty — made the final selection, which has been kept very wide in order not to let any literary taste or way of looking at the world to dominate. Original Prints 3 should be read as a work-in-progress rather than as a definitive statement or showcase. Only by writings becoming public, up for consideration, criticism and rethinking, do they have the opportunity to change and develop.

LORETTA BRESCIANI

Teresa Anderson

MY SISTER TOLD ME

To jack it all in
and become a poet,
pure and simple.
Pattern lines,
Weave and shape and strain
new meanings
out of earthy
everyday words.
I've always written
for posterity,
constructed neat,
impenetrable and defensive
verse which would be
flameproof, shockproof,
oil-resistant, ageless,
like some mythical
stone tablet or the
soles of my brand-new
Doc Marten shoes.

Watching you, I find a way
to fashion something
real and whole
from clay and fire.

Your bowls and vases
will not last forever,
but while they last
they will hold water
beautifully.

2

Vivien M. Adam

from 'COUPLING'

PARTY POLITICS

The politicking particularities
Of the dinner party
Were way above my head.
Sipping the wine, succulating
The duck
Making polite conversation
While I knew the hostess
Wanted my husband
To fuck.

ACCOMPLISHMENT

You only have to look
He said angrily
at this place
To see you haven't done a thing
in days.
You only have to clean
I replied
this place
to achieve even less

SELF OPINION

"That girl is just in love with herself"
My husband said in disgust and lechery
"Clever girl." I said
In envy.

HOWEVER,

I hate the way he blows his nose
in public. I don't particularly
like the way he examines it
in private, either

However,

Last night, in bed,
We stopped doing the crossword
To speedily and enjoyably
make love. Afterwards
I got twenty-two down.
Simple things like that
can be very enjoyable

Sheena Blackhall

THE HONEY THAT CAME FROM THE SEA

Every arching neck in the humid, human circle was craned upward; every gape-mouthed boy was trembling-tight with watching; every lip-sticky, sweet-sucking girl was abrink with thrill; and every, but every eye was fixed with morbid intensity on the tiny, puce-coloured tights of Dolores the high-wire walker, precariously picking a line 200 feet in the air. Hannibal, the wrinkled old Jumbo, slumped like a sack of gigantic oats by a star-spangled drum, trumpeted up a gigantic roar, flapping his cabbage-leaf ears with the force of a blacksmith's bellows. The crowd sighed, a prodded sea anemone, aquiver with delighted alarm, as the little tightrope walker stumbled, losing her concentration, stumbled and wobbled over the dizzying drop.

Would it happen tonight? Would it happen tonight? Would the circus star tumble out of her heavenly certainty and smash in a thousand atoms in the arena dust? How horrible, how dreadful, how splendiferous if she did! The anticipation sent shivers of pleasure rippling through one and all.

The puce-coloured tights with their sparkling of spangles, however, steadied beneath the balancing, outstretched arms, that tilted and swayed, swayed and tilted and settled, like an experienced glider, like the crossed spars of a puppeteer's doll. Had the enthralled spectators been nearer, they might have seen the face of Dolores the tightrope walker turn pale as a pierrot clown beneath the mask of her heavy stage make up and the dove-grey satin leotard that clung to her small breasts rise and fall as rapidly as a captive, fluttering bird in a cage.

An expert seamstress threading a needle of excitement, she was fully alert now. The one near-fatal slip had tautened her caution. The remainder of the act proceeded without further mishap. When she curled one leg, coy as a comma, round the thick rope, and tossed her plumed head till the feathers bounced on a pillow of air; when she slithered lithe as an eel down the rope and kicked it carelessly aside, and bowed her head, as if fencing with death was nothing, the audience rose, rank by rank. Their applause was a burst of exploding fireworks.

Off the high wire the circus girl was quite ungainly; clumsy, even. She walked like a ploughboy, on the balls of her feet. The applause dribbled down to a halt as she clumped off on satin pumps, leaving the animal smells of the tent to Barnet, the seal master, cracking his menagerie to yelps of ecstatic approval.

Saunders the tumbler was waiting for her as usual, in her cream-coloured caravan, the clouds of his fat cigar curling aromatically round her home, a summer nimbus. It was good to relax in the company of a friend, and Saunders was an unobtrusive man. His claims on Dolores' time were slight but pleasant. For, in common with many circus people, the high-wire artist did not care to be tied down or rooted in any way. The shiftless, transitory gypsy life was a fine one, meeting each town afresh, leaving it, before the quality of wonder and exploration had turned sour.

Saunders had half an hour to kill before his turn to enter the arena. He watched the tightrope walker with gentle amusement as she removed successive layers of cosmetic chicanery; like descending a ladder it was, each removal further peeling away another level of spurious grandeur and make-believe. Right down to the bottom rung, to the pastry-pallid cheeks that struck an off-colour note beside the bruised, red, gash of the small, fat lips. Right down to the face, not of Dolores the circus performer, but of Miss Amelia Sotherby-Bates of Whinneyfold, East Worthing, daughter of Jeremy Sotherby-Bates, M.P. for Worthing West, and his wife Mabel-Ann, was terribly fond of babies and terribly fond of good causes, as an M.P.'s wife should be, in Worthing, Watford, or Gjinokastër for that matter. But neither Jeremy Sotherby-Bates, nor Mabel-Ann, had been terribly fond of Amelia, who was supremely indifferent to babies, and cared for good causes not a straw.

She had dismayed her parents by a succession of anti-social activities; had refused to shake hands with sweaty, effusive matrons at church bazaars; had absolutely and categorically dug in her heels and resisted all attempts to cram her dumpy personage into an amenable package of simpering civility at any of her mother's fund-raising functions. In short, Miss Amelia Sotherby-Bates had been a troublesome pain-in-the-ass from the word go, to the World, to Worthing, to everyone, from the day her umbilical cord had knotted itself round her navel. When, therefore, she ran off with a visiting circus, the Sotherby-Bateses had shown an understandable lack of interest in retrieving their disagreeable offspring. They had stitched up the rent in the family fabric caused by the bête-noire's removal in a neat piece of invisible sewing; as if Amelia Sotherby-Bates had never existed, which suited Dolores the tightrope walker down to a Z.

Saunders the tumbler handed her over a last wipe of powder-remover and watched her grimace as the final skin of greasepaint was smeared off.

"That was a close-run thing, tonight, Dolores," he said. The girl shrugged, pouted. She disliked her Amelia face, its plain, pallid contours, its hollow, staring eyes, the crimson slash of its mouth. Under the gold plumes her hair was lank and shapeless. She bent down wearily, unrolling the puce-coloured tights in their glitter of spangles, revealing goose-pimpled legs where the blue veins showed too clearly her tiredness. The satin pumps were replaced by two worn leather sandals. Not one of the audience, seeing her slumped before the mirror in her little caravan, would have given her a glance, let alone a cheer. She was as plain, as uninteresting, as mutton.

"We could go for a drink somewhere. It's a lovely night," said Saunders, though he already knew what her answer would be. He felt it too, when his act was over, that sense of emptiness. Offstage neither had anything left to give. They merely crumpled in on themselves. It was that way with many performers.

The girl felt very shaken. The close brush with catastrophe had affected her more than she cared to admit, even to Saunders. The circus was camped on a stance within five minutes' walk of the sea.

"Not tonight, Saunders," she replied, feeling suddenly rather old. "I think I'd like to stroll a while, on the beach before turning in."

The tumbler nodded, understanding, and walked along a little of the road with her. He stopped, however, at the periphery of the circus area. He never felt completely easy out of the circus boundaries. Across the parched rough grass between the circus and the beach the sun glistened, making the beach shimmer like a ring of Saturn, all fawn and curving, through waves of warmth. Beyond it, the sea lapped and rocked, curiously static, a listener knocking at a door.

"It's very open, the sea," said Saunders the tumbler, quizzically.

"Very open," Amelia agreed. But already she had left him.

At first, the experience of traversing sand, flat and aimless, not tense and tentative as on the high wire, was interesting. Gradually, however, the newness wore off and the circus girl felt lost and useless. Her toe kicked a piece of debris, a broken compass, as if North, South, East or West made any difference to the timeless, directionless, fathomless, surge of the ocean! What navigated the navigators?

After an hour of aimless walking, Amelia lay down on the beach. The sand was soft, warm, neutral, tingling. It was a mingling of thousands of different particles – you couldn't call it a beach, you couldn't lump those tiny fragments of peach-bright flakes together. Each was separate, each sifted through her fingers like seconds in an hour-glass dripping, dripping, running running back . . . She felt like a child again, and began to cover herself up, playing a game with the sand, the vanishing game, covering herself up. . .

When she was dead and buried, when she was buried and dead, would anyone know that Amelia Sotherby-Bates had once run off with a circus to walk the high-wire twice nightly? Indeed, did it matter at all if anyone knew, or if anyone cared? The sea was flat as a mill pond, calm. It seemed to have swallowed the sky. The horizon had quite disappeared.

But not entirely. There was some movement, a stirring of water.

Something was drifting into the shore, something conical, something peculiar. Something was coming out of the sea. That something was floating directly towards Amelia. The tightrope walker flung off the light covering of sand, rose up and walked down to the waters' edge to meet it. She waded into the sea, not noticing its depth, nor its unusual purity, nor the way it hugged and wrapped her around in icy, welcoming waves. The something was clear enough to see, to reach out for, to examine.

The something was a large, gold dish, the size of a town clock-face, and on it, was heaped an anthill, oozing with honey.

"A bee makes honey," thought Amelia Sotherby-Bates, more struck by this thought than by the sight of the gold dish with its cargo of ants sitting lightly on top of the sea.

How busy the ants were! What a miracle of engineering their homes, so close, so close! Yet they never seemed to collide, so industrious, so engrossed in their work, it tired her out to watch them! And the faster they worked, the sweeter grew their honey.

Brown and gold, and everywhere it flowed, from secret inner springs.

"Why are you all so busy?" Amelia asked.

"No time to talk, no time to talk," cried myriad voices. "We have no time for one, in the hill of the ants. Here, each one works for the whole. Thus is our honey sweet. We pool our labours. We have no time for one."

Amelia Sotherby-Bates looked back to the empty beach, looked back across and over the parched, rough grass, to the tinsel minarets of the circus tent where twice-nightly, in puce-coloured tights, Dolores the high-wire walker trod a thin line of glory. She could almost hear the human circle below, willing her feet to fall – the animal baying of their calls, a ring of wolfish teeth.

The smell of the honey was sweet, overpoweringly so. The smallest of steps it was, onto the golden plate, yet the longest, most daring step of her whole life, as she entered the hill of ants. . .

Next morning, the circus found it was lacking a high-wire artist; but someone would always be found to fill the breach, someone hungry for glory, willing to pay the price. And whether the huddle of clothes on the beach belonged to Amelia Sotherby-Bates or Dolores, the tightrope girl or not, was anyone's guess, though Saunders the tumbler certainly thought he knew.

Elizabeth Burns

THE MOTHER BAKES IN THE KITCHEN

the daughter drinks whisky by the fire
when she's finished the glass
she'll go into the kitchen and help

she pours more water into her whisky

the mother's arm is stiff
with stirring the cake mix
quickly, so that the eggs will not curdle it
when it's frothy with air
she sprinkles in cocoa
watches it become
chocolate cake

meanwhile the biscuits are burning
she whisks them out of the oven
levers them onto the cooling tray
lets the air crisp them

she begins to pile the soft chocolate mix
into round greased tins
and thinks as she bakes
of her daughters
childless and rootless
the fiddler, the gardener, the juggler

she thinks of the fiddler
with the tunes of the Highlands
in her fingers and her bow

she thinks of the gardener
with her windowsill of cuttings
and her kitchen full of herbs

she thinks of the juggler
with her pockets full of oranges
travelling to Spain

the mother feels her children
sifting like flour through her fingers

she sees the heat of the baking
steaming up the windows

she sees the mounds of cakes
which will stale before they're eaten

and she wishes for the quick fingers
of the fiddler and her dancing tunes
that can make feet tap or eyes fill with tears

she wishes for the earthy hands
of the gardener digging up weeds
and planting poppy seeds and peach stones

she wishes for the wide stretched arms
of the juggler catching and throwing
keeping all objects in the arc of her body

and she wishes for the way they travel
slipping casually between countries
with only passport and rucksack

and for the way they make love
unhusbanded
not bound by place or time of day

and she wishes for the wicked stepmother
in herself
the disallowed

so she turns off the oven
even though she knows the cakes will sag
and goes to the fireside
and finds her daughter there
who pours her a whisky
and begins to teach her mother
wickedness

BULBS

they're something like the white of hyacinths
coming out from cold wet earth
all those women springing up
arms around the fence
something greening in sunlight

and look, there are daffodils
planted in the shape of a sign of peace
and they're shining their yellow mouths
up at the sun

and the woods around the missile base
are full of earthy smells
pineneedles, hyacinths, woodsmoke

but some soldier's snipped the daffodils
smeared their petals into mud

and in the woods they're driving bulldozers
laying tarmac across campsite circles
crunching as they go at the stalks of hyacinths
making their thick flowers flat

but look, Reagan and Gorbachov
are in a warm room shaking hands
each of them writing their names
on a piece of paper

to say the Cold War's over
and the spring's beginning
and the room is bright with potted plants
forced in some hothouse
to bloom in winter

this is the clean and easy way
to make the world a peaceful place
this is the sensible way

this is not the hard and dirty way
the overnight bus, the tent in the snow
pliers clipping at bits of wire
policemen gripping your arms

and see how simple it was
the base has been emptied of missiles

but once there was a common
wild with flowers

FALLING IN

falling from cliff into ocean a gust lifts you
holds you in air fleet seconds as your mind
gasps at the lush sea mouth and your scared eyes
skim the known grass, cling to clouds before the
fall and splash that gulps you with a green breath
laps you with the milk searching tongues of waves
on wet flesh as your eyes open underwater
to a place of glassiness and you float salt-borne
between fish glint and rings set with limpet
on the intricate fingers of coral and the emerald
banners of seaweed windlessly streaming

and now the seaworld holds you close
lures you with its swell and the daily pull of the moon
kisses you swift and silver, licks your skin
floods you with flash and dapple of fallen light
gathers you in endless folds of ocean's cliffless arms

MOTHER AND CHILD IN THE BOTANIC GARDENS

"Baby carriages are not allowed in the plant houses"

the baby floats carriageless
in her waterlily cradle
it wafts and drifts her round the world

Australasia   Guatemala   Mexico
South Laos   Norfolk Islands   Crete

wrapped in the coir of a coconut
she floats from island to island

a bush with waxy orange flowers
bends between her and the sun
purple berries fall into her lap
she eats them
and lays her head in the creamy pillow
of a lily flower

she is lost in Tropics of the Old World
her dreams are scented

* * * * *

the mother comes running through the plant houses
tropical to temperate and back to tropical
frantic between the arms of palm trees
and the tangle of passion flowers
that curl their tendrils into her hair

fronds of fern tickle and grip
green surrounds her   a mouth of green is
eating her   jade lips
and a moist and mossy tongue
licks her with a limey liquid

cacti crawl at her feet
leer from their gravel and sand
claw their spikes and prickles into her skirts

and the iron skeleton
buckles and caves
its bony fingers
waver in the lily pond

she looks into
its ochre water
and sees
curled on the deck
of a waterlily leaf
her daughter

her eyes gazing up to the glass roof
and her lips
stained with purple

DRIVING DOWN THE M1 THROUGH
WARWICKSHIRE

It's dusk in Shakespeare country, wet June
and hard to slit the sky's cloak, drooped grey cloth
over squelchy earth that snugs the bones of those
who lived within a tiny tightened world
that reached its arms from Orton Water or
the Avon, and beyond that only rumours
blown on grass seeds, telling the city's fables
grown queer, enormous, in repeating.

How would the skin wrinkle on those skeletons
and the eyes, were they to see, become aghast
and the strap of motorway slapped down
over the place of graves, searing oak woods
scurrying with car and lorry monsters
that gulp the leagues to London in the time it
once took to walk to the market and back;
or seeing trousered women, truck driving
sucking from a parchment box the sweet thick
juice of a spikey fruit called pineapple
nibbling pastries from a place named India;
or the inns at the roadside as high as
cathedrals but plain glass windowed, spireless.

Dusk, but Shakespeare's country, and his words have
sown cornfields, heaped harvest in granaries,
give breath to the fluttering heart of the past.

THE PURSUIT OF FIDELITY

(From a 15th century German tapestry
with fidelity depicted as a stag)

They are off out pursuing fidelity again.
He has her mounted on the dappled horse
and the dogs are running through the undergrowth
and the horn is blasting from his lips.

That stag fidelity with its branchy antlers
will surely be caught in the trap
of the looped rope hung between two oaks
blocking the track through the forest.

Then they will have it, he'll shoot the stag
and bring it home, will have the head
with its antlers fastened to the wall
the evidence that in this home, fidelity resides.

But you and I will wander in the forest
climb the mountain, swim in the lake:
no hornblowing, galloping, trampling of flowers
but the stag munching grass, unconcerned.

Susan Chaney

THE SEA UPSTAIRS

When I was a child there were things about my house that I knew for certain. I knew that its name in Cornish was "Uthnoe Veor" and the words would roll heavy and smooth in my mouth like sun warmed pebbles. I knew that in English, this name meant "The House in the Cove". I knew the staircase had sixteen stairs, because my sister counted me up and down them. I knew the way the sunlight fell through the fanlight above the front door making shallow fonts of soft yellow light for me to wriggle my toes in. These things were facts, they were a part of me.

There were other things about my house that I only suspected or sensed with some inner, watching self. It was 1955 but I believed that we were still at war with Germany. The War still seemed to haunt my parents' lives. I believed it inhabited the dining room along with my mother's pain. This room was rarely used, there was something mysterious about it, something forbidden. I loved to creep in when my mother was busy in the kitchen. Lying under the massive mahogany table, in the closed, musty darkness which smelled faintly of ripe apples and lavender polish, I was always listening for the whine of the bombs. Always watching for the spirals of black smoke as the Spitfires climbed into the blue, vacant sky. My skin would cringe as it waited for the impact, the crumpling timbers, the deadly splinters of flying glass.

Every Tuesday, my mother cleaned the brass and silver and as we sat together at the table, she applying the polish and me dutifully buffing up the colour with a pair of my sister's worn out knickers, she would reminisce about the war years when my father was posted overseas. She would tell me about dances she had been to in a ballroom where the walls were hung with mirrors. She would describe in detail dresses she had worn and when I screwed my eyes tight shut, I would see her as she had been then, gay, provocative, slender as a reed in her black silk dress. On her dark hair, an absurd, frivolous concoction of scarlet velvet and feathers. Sometimes she would bend her head confidingly toward me and tell me of a boy she had loved.

"Do you know," she said, "He always brought me a corsage of lilies and he would fasten them to my dress himself."

A corsage of lilies. How wonderful it sounded. I would see my mother in her finery turning in Freddie's arms, she so willing and he, sleek as a seal in his dark suit and patent leather dancing pumps. Watching her thin, bluish hands with their prominent veins grow quiet and drop from their work, I would struggle with the enormous question of who I was. If my mother had married Freddy and they had a little girl, would she be me? Sometimes I imagined the pair of them bending over a child with a short, red dress and long yellow plaits. She looked exactly like Elizabeth Perfect, one of my deadliest enemies, the kind of child I hated. The kind who never tore their clothes or climbed a tree. If this child were me, where would I be? Would I even exist at all?

The other thing I believed about my house was that the sea lived upstairs in the bedrooms. When my mother showed visitors the house she would invariably shrug her shoulders, sigh with exasperation and say, "What other man but my husband would buy a house in Cornwall that didn't have a view of the sea?"

Listening to her I would flush, open my mouth to protest, but the words and colour would die a quick, hopeless death. It was useless. I knew it.

I would turn instead to the window pane where the salt made beautiful opaque patterns. I would touch the faded curtains with my tongue and they tasted of seaweed and salt. Every crack in the floorboards was stuffed with grains of sand. The sea never slept and at night, I listened to the slow rhythm of the waves as they climbed and fell against the pink stained walls of my room.

The summer that I was twelve, Miles, Melissa and Miranda came to live in what once had been Jimmy Tremain's barn. I knew at once they were different to all the other children in the village. For one thing, they didn't have a father and for another, they didn't own any playclothes. They wore their schoolclothes even on the hottest day. Identical, royal-blue sweaters and socks. The girls with pleated, grey skirts and Miles with long, grey shorts, worn thin and shiny at the backside, but always neatly pressed; three pairs of knees with the coarse, corrugated skin, very pale pink, and covered in short, stumpy, blond hairs, made me think of piglets, rooting and wriggling in the straw. They had large, domed foreheads with lank blond hair and their transparent blue eyes swam in their faces like jellyfish.

Their mother was a slow-moving, armour-plated creature. With her stern, jutting bosom and helmet of lacquered hair, there was something majestic about her. She reminded me of a figurehead on the prow of some mighty sailing ship as she steered her family through the treacherous waters of loneliness and defeat. She was extremely vulnerable, being both a "Foreigner" from London and because she lived without a man. In the village, speculation was furious about her absent husband. There were more words for me to ponder, unknown words with their curious passion, their intrigue and their power: words like Adultery. Embezzlement. Debtor. Suicide.

I was fascinated by Miles, Melissa and Miranda. I think I always knew that tragedy was touching them.

It was a warm, innocuous afternoon when Melissa drowned. As I stared at the tiny, blanket-covered corpse, Paul Laity supplied the details, his carroty face bobbing up and down like a balloon on a string. He looked curiously one-dimensional, spindly, white and jerking.

"I seed her when they got her from the water. Twas all slime and seawater pouring from her nose and lugs."

Then I turned and saw Miles crouched on the sand.

"I tried to save her," he kept on saying.

"I tried to save her, but I couldn't reach her."

I imagined his desperate arms threshing the water to white. When he raised his face, his forehead was pitted with silica and blood. The bland, anxious schoolboy was gone forever. An awful authority stood in his eye.

It was never the same after that. The days of warm paddling in ruched costumes bagging with sand were gone forever. Soon, men came to install life-saving equipment and scarlet flags flew a warning from the rocks. On a large wooden board, white letters screamed from red paint.

BATHING IS STRICTLY FORBIDDEN FROM THIS BEACH.

All I really remember about Melissa's funeral is the smell of my mother's suede coat. It was such a beautiful coat, slender

and neat with a half slung belt at the back and it was a
wonderful shade of conker-brown that would lighten and
darken again as I stroked it this way and that with my fingers. It
smelled moist and cool like mud. She had promised to give it to
me when I was fourteen.

That night I couldn't sleep, I kept hearing that desperate little
sentence.

"I couldn't reach her. I couldn't reach her."
The water was running through the old lead pipes and as I
listened it turned to rustling birds, to footsteps and finally to the
voice of the Minister winging from the pulpit.

"Christ, have mercy upon us."
The solemn reply from the congregation:

"Lord, have mercy upon us."
"Oh Christ, have mercy upon us."
I ran my hands across my belly, over the bones in my hips. In
biology, at school, we were learning about the reproductive
system. The teacher had told us that every girl child is born with
all the eggs she would ever shed, intact inside her ovaries. I
thought of Melissa's body sliced open, showing all her eggs.
Would they be soft foaming clouds like frogspawn or tiny hard
frosted silver balls like the ones we used to decorate the
Christmas cake? No wriggling, insistent little sperm would ever
fertilize them now. I would grow. I would become a woman, but
Melissa would always be ten years old with her sharp little
bones, her bitten fingers and her shallow chest.

I left my room and crept into my mother's bedroom. I swung
open the wardrobe and took down her suede coat. I slipped it on
over my thin nightdress, my nipples puckering at the touch of
the cold slippery lining. My breasts were just beginning to swell
and soon I would no longer be able to pretend that I was a boy.
Soon I would be like my sister with a first bra and lipstick and
hours of anxious inspection behind the bathroom door.

I didn't want to be fourteen. I didn't want to inherit my
mother's coat. I didn't want her look of resignation or her
perpetual little frown. The coat slithered to the floor as I ran
from the house and I left it slumped at the foot of the stairs.

The tide was out, the sand stretched endless, pitted and
wrinkled by the waves, hard-edged beneath my feet. I went
unresisting, drawn like iron filings to the moon. I passed the
huddle of people-shaped rocks I used to play among. My feet
were chanting,

"It's still my place. It's still my place." I was still at home here, despite the betrayal, the treacherous current that webbed Melissa and sucked her down. I touched one of the rocks, my hand lying flat, the fingers spread wide. The crusty limpets pushed upwards into my palm. The fruity smell of the seaweed washed over me.

"I still have the power," I said. "Once I brought you to life when I was lonely. I made you my friends. I still have the power."

I knelt beside them on the sand. Suddenly I wanted to know everything. What exactly was the colour of the sand? In the summer night, it looked grey, mysterious, it was faintly blushed like pewter. Was it grey or green or silver? Why was my mother so unhappy? Why had Melissa drowned? Why was my childhood slipping away from me?

I jumped up and ran down to the edge of the sea. Slowly I began to turn as I had so often done before. Faster and faster I went, my arms stretched rigid for balance. The moonlight and the lights from the boats moored out in the bay merged together until they fell through my hands like bright satin ribbons. I was dizzy and breathless with speed and then I felt the most enormous power growing inside me. My arms felt limitless as though I could stretch out past the steep, crooked red rocks, past the sleeping houses until I reached the windows of my parents' room. I could reach between them in that lonely bed. Illuminate their sleeping faces. I could restore the colour to my mother's faded dresses. I could even make her dance again. More than this, I could reach beyond them over the tangled churchyard wall and excavate Melissa's grave. I would touch her drowned, white face sunk in its cushion of ivory silk. I would raise her from the dead.

My arms lifted, a flight of owls, gold, white and tawny against the sky. I knew then that I was losing the child that I had been. It was time to travel on. The world spun, crazy all around me until I fell in a huddle and felt the warm, glassy waves lapping at my legs, pulling like a woman spinning thread.

Then at last I knew that the rocks were only rocks. That Melissa was really dead and above me, my parents slept, having made their own uneasy peace with the past. My head hummed like a telephone wire. It was my first taste of freedom.

Maud Devine

'FROM THE WOODPILE'

A SONNET FOR EDWIN MORGAN

See you, Mister Edwin Morgan
Trowel away man, label the lairs of our history
Defrost our post-glacial soil and mould it into poetry
There's still a drama to dig from this graveyard comedian
Your sonnets are tickets on a Greater Somewhere Tardis
Through rainswept quarries grey with the shadow of Culloden
Via stratification in shark-infested Bearsden
To the sky, no limit, landing in a lunar terminus
Time-lord, pocket full of thistle seeds
You left us listening for a horn, hearing only an echo
You've zipped into your vacuum suit to the moon to sow
A golden harvest or another planet of weeds
Born in the wind which blows a trumpet over Jericho
The thistle down roots into the fallen walls to grow

SOCKIN OOR

Auld gang there oot, I grein the hain
o yer wid like a scart afore the flaw
In yer cranreuchie neuk coorie me sain
when the fleechin day turns tae snaw
In the sockin oor by the sklentin licht
rigwiddie carlin shadows flee
I hae the waff o Auld Shankie smookin in the nicht
tae gansch gouls but his weird disne daunton me
De'il tak ma rickle o banes, ma hool
fur yer kail brose, and the warld toom caup, yer baw
tae play heidies in the pit daurk nevermas o the mools
sin doon the unco loan I maun gang awa
Fey jauds, deed lichts, fior, I dinne fear
but the wid's geens, starn sheens, I shall miss sair sweir

NATURAL PHILOSOPHY

There's a time and a place
for everything
and in gardening
the earthworm toils
beneath the soil
eats dirt brakes ground
can't see the flowers
for the birds and the bees
anyway
not hooked on fishing
he bores they pollinate
naturally

AN IBIS

She's dedicated to writing
the hieroglyphics on the wall
not at all what you'd expect
an evanescent
swan in flight
manifest
in the tremble of a leaf
but a quaint fat wader
sharp-billed
used to standing
on one leg
spearing and regurgitating
in a muddy river

* Ibis – sacred bird in Ancient Egypt dedicated to Thoth, god of writing.

THE SISTER

The sister stays
behind the gate
white flag waving
to her Sunday family
revving back
to a distant main road
She turns inward
overshadowed
by the slow growing holly
still green as the wreaths
of her nineteenth Christmas
A lamp stays lit
within her room
a cell to keep
each night vigil
black mould creeps
where the chestnut branch
thrusts through the roof
She has many locks
but can not stop
the tree snaking
through fissures in the stone

THE AVENUE

Grey stone
terraced houses
stand
elite troops
front rank
at attention
for dames to approve
windows' gleam
and precisely cut
squares of grass
earth borders hoed
the fourth Sunday
of every month
Tea roses are pruned
An appropriate few
but not too many
flowers bloom

REGENERATION

Remember man that thou art dust
and into dust thou shalt return
and return and return and return
fire burn and cauldron bubble
So when shall we three meet again?
April showers May flowers
or the petrified forest
mackintosh out in case of sun
me and me and . . .
a syphillitic dinosaur
smoking his copy of EHT SEMIT
and ogling extinct men in glass cases

Anne Downie

DEADLY SIN

Maeve raised her leg a fraction off the floor then sat back on her heels to ease the pain. Her hand felt the indentation on her knee where a ridge on the rough stone had cut into the second Sorrowful Mystery. She eyed the distance between herself and the healing strip of carpet in front of the hearth. Two black cats and Dympna, the half-dog, lay stretched out, impervious to the hallowed air around them.

A rebuking finger stabbed her in the shoulder. The girl turned round to find Aunt Bridget fixing her with a disapproving glare while scarcely pausing for breath in the rhythmic chanting of the Hail Mary. Offering her sacrifice up for the Holy Souls, Maeve, once again, placed her knee in the position of torture. By the end of the Rosary, she felt an entire battalion of souls must be winging their way Heavenward, courtesy of her endurance.

"Prayer for the Pope's intention," said her mother, launching into the "Our Father".

"Prayer for Willie Joe McCann," mumbled Uncle Seumas.

"And Maura McShane, who's overdue," his sister added, not to be outdone.

"Prayer for King Edward to give up that married woman," Aunt Bridget intoned, throwing herself into the "Memorare" with a relish totally lacking in religious fervour. That the Duke of Windsor had made his choice many years before was no reason, in Aunt Bridget's estimation, for admitting defeat.

When the spiritual needs of what seemed like half the villagers of Ballymoran and their former Sovereign had been attended to, Maeve was the first to rise, rubbing her now misshapen knee.

"Be sure and confess your distraction to Canon Brady!" Aunt Bridget's tight little mouth almost smiled, anticipating the severity of the old priest's penance.

"Indeed and I won't!" Maeve responded spiritedly. "I was kneelin' on a bump! My knee was in agony!"

"Our Blessed Lord had nails through His!" Bridget's tone suggested, somehow, that Maeve had personally wielded the mallet!

The girl bit back an angry reply. With a sense of victory, Bridget picked up Dympna and tucked the dog under her bony arm. Maeve turned her head away. The dog's mutilated stumps always aroused a feeling of revulsion within her. That dog is disgustin'! She almost spoke her thoughts aloud. It should have been put down right after the accident!

The memory of that day had etched itself deeply in Maeve's young mind, Aunt Bridget's hysterical screams drowning out Uncle Seumas's earnest protestations.

"I didn't see her, Bridget . . . How could I?" . . . then "You knew I was threshing! You shouldn't have let her run wild!"

Bridget's ears were deaf to his words. The weight of grief and guilt made her sink to the ground. The pathetic bundle of matted fur whimpered in her arms as she rocked back and forth. Seumas turned on his heel and left. Bridget cradled the dog to her breast, wrapping it in her cardigan which was quickly suffused with a bright red stain. A hand reached out for the dog. Seumas was back, hunting rifle under his arm. "Come on, Bridget! Let me put her out of her misery!" Bridget's cry of rage witnessed that her senses had returned.

Over the next few months, she nursed the dog back to health, lavishing all the love and attention once sealed within her body. A love that might have been given to her child, if she could have overcome her fear of men. Bridget's obsessional devotion was now directed at Dympna. The unfortunate animal was subjected to the changing whims of an ageing spinster, who dressed it daily in a variety of ribbons and necklaces; a fate no whole dog would hang around long enough to endure.

Maeve hadn't actually said she was going to Benediction, she told herself, as she quickened her step past the goose-pen. It wasn't her fault if that's what they all assumed! A hissing noise behind her told her she'd been spotted. She broke into a run as the irate mother, yellow balls of fur teetering drunkenly in her wake, temporarily abandoned her brood to give chase.

"HERE, JUMP!" a voice shouted as she struggled with the wire catch over the gate post. Her arms were grabbed and she was hoisted over. Charlie let go his grip and grinned at her. On the other side of the gate, her pursuer hissed and spat impotently.

"If that was mine," said Charlie, indicating the goose, "I'd have her with spuds!"

"She's O.K.!" Maeve shrugged.

"Is she hell!" Charlie was vehement. "She near had the ankles off us!"

"She thinks you're after her goslings, that's all." Maeve walked away, fearful that she could be seen from Aunt Bridget's room, at the back of the house.

"She's wrong there," he grinned. "It's you I'm after! ... Didn't think you'd come!"

"And why wouldn't I?" Maeve's tone was defiant.

"Ah, well ... you see ... I'm really dangerous ... Not just a huffer and puffer like your oul' goose there!"

"Don't believe you!" She looked hard at him for evidence to the contrary.

"And why not?" He pulled her down beside him on the grass. She was grateful for the large oak tree obscuring them from prying eyes.

"Just a feeling." Despite her words, she edged away slightly, keeping a respectable distance between them.

"You think they put you away for missin' Mass, do you?" The smile had left his face.

"They haven't 'put you away'. It's not prison!"

"What would you call Saint Peter's Reformatory, then?" A note of bitterness had crept into his voice.

"Well ... I mean ... I don't see any guards over you."

"Said I needed a pee! There's some things they let you do on your own!"

Maeve's clandestine meetings with Charlie became a nightly occurrence. "They'll be thinkin' I've a weak bladder!" he laughed. She found it easy to talk to him, and as for Charlie, Brother Dominic would have been amazed! "A fella of few words" was how he labelled the boy, but with Maeve, he really opened up. He even told her of his crime, something that had been locked in the dark recesses of his mind, for the four years since it happened.

He'd meant to kill his father, no matter what they said! When Charlie heard screams and saw his sisters cowering in terror that night, nothing "snapped in his fourteen year old mind", as his Defence put it. Instead, he saw what he had to do with chilling clarity. He was a good shot. He had to be! His markmanship had to put food in the family's belly, since their meat money regularly lined the till in Frank Dougan's public house. He'd killed dozens of rabbits, but a man was different. You had to hit the right spot. He looked at his mother's cut lip and swollen eye, then took quick, but careful, aim, as his father lunged towards him. A line from "Macbeth", learnt at school, came incongruously into the boy's mind . . . "Yet who would have thought the old man to have so much blood in him." His only regret was that his sentence in the Remand Home meant his mother was denied the family's only potential wage earner. She would have to scrape a living for them on her own. But sure hadn't she always done that! His father had squandered what little they had. The family had wanted for everything. At least now, they could live without terror.

It wasn't until Maeve was making up the pig fodder, almost two months later, that she realised retribution for her sin had been exacted. As she squeezed the hot potatoes through her fingers, carefully mixing in the bran, her stomach heaved. She ran out of the boiler room and gulped in lungfuls of fresh air. The sickly sweet smell of the bran mash drifted through the open door, and a fresh wave of nausea hit her.

"What's the matter with you?" Bridget appeared suddenly in the yard in front of her, Dympna tucked, as usual, under her arm.

"Nothing!" Maeve turned away. Dympna's aquamarine beads always reminded her of the poster in Miss McNulty's geography class, "The Bay of Naples". She tried to concentrate hard on that beautiful blue-green sea, forcing the memory of the animal feed from her mind.

"Hm . . . she's a funny colour, isn't she, my love?" The dog closed her eyes in complete indifference.

"I'm hungry, that's all!" Maeve crossed the yard quickly, anxious to distance herself from her inquisitor.

"Breakfast's on the table. No thanks to you, Miss. You were supposed to set the table, first thing!" Her aunt hurried to catch up with her, lest her barbs missed their mark. Maeve slipped into place beside Uncle Seumas, who was already wolfing a huge plate of fried eggs, bacon and potato bread. Egg yolk was running down his grizzled chin. Her mother put a plate in front of her. As she looked down at the eggs floating in their little pool of grease, she felt her gorge rise. She was too late to reach the door before the contents of her stomach hit the floor.

35

She would go to Scotland to have the baby! It was the only answer. If the Sweeney family were to hold their heads high in Ballymoran, then not a soul, bar the Canon, must know of Maeve's fall from grace. After the bitter recriminations had passed, Aunt Bridget was galvanised into action. She hurried down to Saint Saviour's Church, returning fifteen minutes later with Canon Brady. Seumas excused himself embarrasedly while Bridget and Maeve's mother went into conference in the front parlour, a conference from which the person, top of the agenda, was entirely excluded.

While her fate was being decided. Maeve slipped out of the house. The Reform boys would be working at Willie Burns's farm. She must get word to Charlie. The father had a right to know! As luck would have it, Charlie, and a younger weedy-looking boy, were smoking behind the hut, which served as a toilet. His face lit up when he saw her.

"Keep a look-out Andy!" He shouted back at the youth, as he ran up the meadow to meet her. He seemed delighted at the news, and appeared not to notice her distress. "A baby . . . our baby! God, that's wonderful!"

"How could it happen, Charlie? We only did it the once . . . and not really . . . not properly!" Maeve was angry at his apparent unconcern.

He held her hands. "Listen to me, Maeve . . . now listen! I love you, . . . d'you hear me? I love you and I'm going to marry you. Our baby's going to have a proper home. I'll be gettin' out the Reform and we'll . . ."

He was cut short by the look-out's hoarse, but insistent, call.

"Charlie, quick! He's comin'!"

Brother Frederick was striding towards them, an angry scowl on his face.

"You boys there . . . get back to work AT ONCE!"

"Don't worry, darlin'. It'll be O.K.," Charlie whispered, as he walked away. Brother Frederick stared disapprovingly after Maeve's retreating figure.

Charlie's assurances now seemed hollow to Maeve, as she leaned over the deck-rail of the ship, trying to get a last glimpse of the Irish coastline. They had kept her at home until she began to "show". Uncle Seumas ran her to the ship, hardly exchanging a word throughout the journey. His silence, she was sure, was embarrassed rather than censorious.

Glasgow seemed a grey noisy place after the fields of Bally-moran. As they rattled through the streets in her Uncle John's van, narrowly missing two fat women, who seemed, in common with a number of its citizenry, to have some sort of death-wish, he blethered on, in sharp contrast to the journey she'd passed with Seumas.

"Ah jist wish you could stey wi' us, hen! You'd be very welcome. You know that! But we huvnae the room!" He was right! Maeve was mortified when she saw her three little cousins cramped in the one bed, to accomodate her overnight stop.

"Don't you worry about that, darlin'. Sure they enjoy it," Her mother's sister reassured her. Despite her assurances, Aunt Teresa spent a great part of the evening trying to stop their "carry-on". The sound of sharp smacks added to their guest's discomfiture.

Maeve found it impossible to sleep. Her aunt's house was on a busy main road. Tramcars clanged past the bedroom window half the night. It sounded as if they were driving around the room. She got up to close the window, which was level with the passengers on the trams' top deck. She thought they couldn't see her in the darkened bedroom, but one cheery young lad blew her a kiss, which sent her scurrying back to bed. His smile had reminded her of Charlie's, and the memory brought hot stinging tears to her eyes.

She felt exhausted in the morning, as Uncle John ran her to the convent, her home for the remainder of the confinement.

"Noo, if you need onythin', Maeve . . . onythin' at aw, hen, jist ring this number. It's the work. The foreman'll make sure I get the message!" He embraced her roughly and handed her case to the young nun who opened the door.

"She'll be hunky-dory! Won't she Sister?" The nun smiled in silent affirmation and glided off down a corridor, Maeve in tow. The place smelled of a peculiar mixture of wax polish and incense. The young nun showed her to a simply furnished room. Its only decoration was a picture of Jesus in his dying agony; a crown of thorns on his head. She thought at first the eyes were closed, but when she looked again, they appeared to open. There was an inscription underneath which read:
NO MATTER WHERE YOU STAND IN RELATION TO THIS PAINTING, THE EYES OF THE SAVIOUR WILL ALWAYS FOLLOW YOU.

That's about all I'm needin'! Maeve thought, wearily.

The time there passed slowly. Maeve was grateful when the nuns agreed to let her help out in their hospital. Giving out magazines and tea made the long lonely days endurable. The convent grounds were beautiful, though. The nuns had built a simple grotto where various statues to the saints were housed, each with its own small patch of shaded garden. You could sit there amongst the scent of flowers, with only the bees for company, and imagine you were hundreds of miles from the city.

It was while Maeve was sitting in Saint Joseph's own little horticultural haven, that her waters broke. She was early! True, she'd been feeling twinges, but she'd been experiencing so many different sensations lately, that it was hard to differentiate between them. She'd been feeling the baby pushing against the limits of its cramped space for some time now, and used these private moments in the grotto to talk soothingly to him. She felt certain he was a boy! She had been in the midst of one of those secret conversations when the floodgates opened, quite unexpectedly. She felt a sudden terror, as if the baby was going to be washed away in the tide coming from within her. An elderly nun, Sister Cecilia, busy hanging out the washing, heard the girl's cries and hurried towards her, as fast as her arthritic feet would allow.

The next few hours were a confusion of pain, bright lights and sheer exhaustion. Nuns shouted conflicting instructions at her . . . "PUSH . . . No, don't bear down just yet. Hold on . . Come on now, one FINAL PUSH . . . and AGAIN, . . . that's it!"

Then a feeling of immense relief, as if years of constipation were at an end.

Maeve heard her baby cry, a weak but insistent sound. She struggled to raise her head, in time to see a masked and gowned nun, carrying the wrapped little bundle, now crying lustily, from the room.

"My baby! I want my baby!"

"Now, now, my dear," a kindly, but unfamiliar nun's face loomed over her. "It's for the best!"

It was then that she gave way to the tears that had been welling inside her for nine months. She was never to see her baby. She'd agreed, albeit unwillingly to give him up.

"You're only sixteen, now, Maeve. Your whole life is before

you!" the Canon had argued, in a voice unused to being challenged.

"Best that it goes to a good Catholic home!" Aunt Bridget had declared firmly. There was absolutely no way she was going to have their shame paraded before the whole parish! Bernadette Flynn, President of the Union of Catholic Mothers, and Maura Divers, second cousin to His Grace, the Archbishop, no less, (and didn't she let you know it) would have a field-day! Maeve's mother, fully dependent on her sister-in-law's charity for the roof over their heads, had wrung her hands, but turned away from the girl's silent plea.

"Now the Sisters know of many well set up couples, whom God, in His wisdom, has chosen not to give the blessing of children," Canon Brady had said finally, as he patted her hand.

"They'll give the babby all the things it needs!"

They wouldn't give it what she could! Its own mother's love. At that thought, she cried, as though her heart would break; terrible racking sobs which shook her whole body and left her feeling exhausted and bereft.

Charlie was fully aware of the risk he was taking, but he had to see her. Now that it was Spring, they were back helping with the lambing.

"We won't be doing the Sweeney farm, this time round," was all Brother Dominic had said. There wasn't much more he could have told them. Bridget Sweeney had merely sent a brief note, saying that, "as they were using other local help", the boys' services would no longer be required.

"I see Maeve Sweeney's back," Charlie had overheard the fella who did the chicken sexing say to Willie Burns.

"Aye! I don't think Scotland was to her taste," their employer had answered.

No mention of a baby there! He had to find out for himself! Charlie had never had anything of his own. The mere thought of seeing his own flesh and blood had sustained him through the last few months. He bent low, as he skirted the hedge between the Burns and Sweeney farms.

He was crossing the yard when Bridget saw him. Dympna had let out a half-hearted bark, which died away quickly, as if the effort had been too much for her.

"Hey, you there! Just a minute! Where d'you think you're goin'?"

"I'm lookin' for somebody!" Charlie peered in the farmhouse window, at an empty room.

"You're a Reform boy, aren't you? You've no business to be here! Get off our land! . . . D'you hear me?"

Charlie crossed and looked in the byre. "Not till I've seen Maeve!"

A look of dawning realisation came over Bridget's face.

"Jesus, Mary and Joseph! YOU'RE the one!"

Charlie spun round and gripped her arm fiercely. "Where is she? And where's my baby?"

"Your baby!" Bridget almost spat the words at him. "What right have you to call a baby yours?"

Maeve was in the dairy, churning the butter, when she heard the voices, raised in anger. It couldn't be . . . She ran out, scattering squawking hens from her path, and saw Charlie facing Aunt Bridget, fighting desperately to control the rage building within him. He turned, and his face changed as he saw her.

"Maeve . . . Maeve . . . are you all right?"

"Charlie, they wouldn't let me keep the baby. She made me give him away!" Maeve broke down in tears.

"YOU BITCH!" Charlie shouted at Bridget. "YOU BLOODY BITCH! . . . What right had you . . ."

"Every right!" Bridget cut him short, a steely glint in her eyes. "You're a criminal . . . a common criminal! Just thank God your son has a home with people fit to look after him!"

"I'll get you for this!" Charlie's face was white with anger.

"Don't you threaten me!" Bridget was now in control. "You took advantage of an innocent young girl. If you come here again, I'll make sure they lock you up and throw away the key!"

"I'll get you!" Charlie shouted over his shoulder, as he ran out of the yard. "You better watch out! D'you hear me!"

For the next few days, Bridget never let Maeve out of her sight. Charlie's threats did not scare her. What really frightened her was the thought of her niece committing deadly sin . . . with a Reform boy! The Blessed Virgin would weep tears of blood at the very thought. As a self-appointed moral sentinel, she stuck closer to Maeve than her guardian angel. When Maeve went to collect the eggs, Bridget was right there, holding the pail. When she went down to the long meadow to fetch the cows for milking, Bridget came too, almost running to keep up with her niece's long strides.

"Where are you off to?" Bridget stopped in her search for Dympna, whom Seumas's black and white collie, Finn, had been persistently sniffing round. The girl was turning out of the yard.

"Goin' for water," Maeve replied, "The pump's actin' up again!"

Bridget had to make a quick decision. To seek out the dogs from whichever barn they were bespoiling, and boot Finn to ensure he finally got the message, or keep up her vigilance.

"You shouldn't lift any weights till your insides have healed!" She took one of the pails from the girl's hand. The dogs could wait! Maeve was unsure whether her aunt was being genuinely solicitous, believing, as she did, that childbirth was a form of illness. Or was this just another attempt to keep her under surveillance? Not that it mattered! She was beyond caring.

They entered the meadow, where the pool, used as their emergency supply, was situated. The water was brown and brackeny, but, providing you boiled it long enough, the tea it made was drinkable. Maeve hung onto a bush with one hand, and bent over the pool, pail in hand. Something bright and blue, like the Bay of Naples, was glinting on the bottom. Bridget saw it at the same time. Before Maeve could stop her, her aunt plunged waist deep into the murky water. Bending forward, she thrust her arms below the surface, then, uttering a terrible cry, like an animal in pain, she held aloft the pathetic form of Dympna, water cascading from the dog's lifeless body.

Gerrie Fellows

'ACROSS THE BORDER'

IN MACFARLANE COUNTRY

I   The Skier

We've come up
  under the steel thicket
              of powerlines
Our plastic boots smacking
                    the asphalt
Over the crest of the road
          framed by a wigwam
sways a day-glo orange Indian

The wigwam becomes a set of skis
The skier
  squints from his neoprene hood
The cause of his lopsided gait
his unclipped boots

We nod in passing   long metres
before snow   Wondering at him
as he heads
                down
                    to Inveruglas
and we strike over the bridge
into grass and bracken

II   Winter

My boot without its crampon
slips   I move up awkwardly
(out of habit with winter)

Tom above a high step watching
snarled at
        taps his way out of earshot

Ice   rock   clutched root
Axe sunk into turf
my boot   miraculously solid
on its hewn black shelf   I'm up
tottering over skiddy grass

Beyond the gully   perched
on a boulder on the edge
of failure   above the country
my people once came from
I fumble with the crampon straps
and weep

But edged   my boots unlock
the winter

III   Gold

Below me
the reservoir slops chopped steel
over its drowned glen

Wood rots
Iron rusts

My body sings
        its way back from spindrift
Fake white angles pitched into air
An axe planted into the north
Myself   without reserves   its flag

Flicked rain
Leeward and southward
Water and islands
Blue light struggles to break

and a rainbow arcs to its golden end
not in Macfarlane country   but
above the closed hotel at Inversnaid

NORTH AND SOUTH

In my mind's eye the lorries
move into the greeny haunch of
the border hills past Elvanfoot
My life   strung between places
north and south

Through the spat colours of metal
and laughter   arriving
rucksack over one shoulder
to a southern evening

That was not the story   There
are journeys without lightness

I stepped from a car at the gate
                not knowing   where
in all those wings and wards and
flowerbeds and white coats and
men shutting women up   she was

On a late afternoon pathway
it was she who met me   saying
I'm okay   which was not the truth
but a part of the truth
as this was   a kind of homecoming

HOMECOMING

The flat was tidy but she wanted to clean
She wiped the cooker   the worktop
the shiny cylindrical saucepans
Through the skylight   the sun
was a brazen shower

He said   You don't have to do that
The sunlight blew bronze bubbles

She said   You won't listen to me
He said   The drugs are wearing off
I thought   But it's her place

The sunlight flew about the leaves

It was important to take back crisp
clean clothes   I stood
at the ironing board in her attic bedroom
green light flicking the window
out of practice   clumsily manoeuvring
the iron over pastel folds   sick
with the steamy heat   thinking
that this was love

Janice Galloway

BREAKING THROUGH

From the outside you would never have known. People passed in the street and never looked up. All they saw was the boarded-up shop, the empty flat next door, the open close mouth swallowing in to the dark. But if you went in, feeling through, you saw a square of light high on the end wall, reflecting a shape of itself down on the grey stone steps. The steps had cream edges. They curved and rose to her own front door and opposite, the Sisters' door. The Sisters were very old and indistinct: powdery faces in fur coats, spindly ankles hanging beneath. Their eyes smeared behind thick glasses. They never spoke.

But from outside, there was no hint of the two rooms of their people, perched over the hollow shape that had sold tobacco and sweets, daily news. They were virtually secret.

There was more.

To reach it, you had to ignore the stone steps and meet the darkness at the flat butt-end of the close. Then you screwed your eyes up tight and there was a brown door with a latch. You lifted the latch and the light spread in a triangle over the paving and you could see. Straight in front, the green hedge like a surprise and the grass. Over your shoulder, the car noises, the talk and whistling of people, widening and fading as they passed, and you in the dark with the unsuspected grass and birds and sky. It was better not to wait too long here. Sometimes the wind would come and slam off the blue and green and leave you alone in the deep brown of the close, a stinging hand where the door had been. It was better to slip through and shut the door quickly behind, then turn round and stand in this new place with the garden and the slab path at your feet that took you to Bessie's on the left, the wash-house on the right. Furthest away, the wall that made a boundary of the cemetery. Fingers of obelisks, the tips of tombstones behind the hang of some unidentifiable tree. The two houses, the wall and the hedge made a square and filled it with grass. The brown strips up the sides made Bessie's garden: she had wallflowers. The grass was a drying green and a place for sitting. The Sisters made no claims on it so there was an easy share between Bessie, Janet and her mother. And Blackie. Blackie was Bessie's cat.

Janet visited Bessie at regular times and sometimes other times in between. Most often they sat together in the low front room with a cup of tea each and some biscuits or slices of cake on a plate. Plain cake. Behind their backs, the bedroom that Janet had never seen, at the other side, the space with the cupboards and the ring for cooking, the place where you washed cups. The three rooms made a row, like square beads on a string. They were always in the middle of the row, the living room where all the space was filled with big furniture. Bessie would squeeze through with the tea to the chairs at the fire and after that they didn't move. They didn't speak much either. Bessie was not conversational and Janet was shy. Bessie was old with rolled up hair in a circle round her head and lines on her neck like a tortoise. She was small and thin. Janet was merely six. The attraction in going was not the house or the old woman. The attraction was Blackie. Blackie was lithe and straightforwardly dark till he rolled over. His underside was shock-white. Green eyes, pink ears like a rabbit's inside and white whiskers. You could count them. The main thing about Blackie was NOT TO TOUCH. Janet wanted to touch but didn't. It was good to watch him but better when he rubbed against bare ankles or jumped to make a nest on a carefully stilled lap. That wasn't often. Janet sometimes watched him playing in the garden, and, if Bessie was not there, stroked his warm white underneath as he stretched on the grass. This never eased the wanting though, it was never enough. What Janet wanted was more than that. As though she wanted to feel the essence of the fur, absorb it through the skin til it was wrapped about the bone and part of herself. The want was sore. And the want was always most in Bessie's front room with Blackie on the rug looking into the fire.

Bessie never said much. She was dour, her mother said. Terse. This much was a solid, a reassuring nub in their relationship. There had to be something badly wrong then, the day Bessie shouted from the door then rushed up beside her as she played on the grass, arms knitting at nothing, eyes searching for something she couldn't see. Janet knew to follow, fast-moving now the words had stopped, over the grass and brown borders, the weedy slabs to the door and inside, past the cabinet and armchairs.

There was the usual tan-colour of the fire surround, the ornamental brasses on the mantelpiece. Inside, a black-backed roaring fire. And inside that, framed in flames, the upright vase of the black cat, sizzling in a mound of coals. The fur was catching slowly, jets budding along the dark outline as he sat: front legs taut and tail curled over the paws, head high with the ears in points, their pinkness glinting in the reflected light. Sheathed in golden-hearted arrows of flame, Blackie burned. His eyes were full as green moons.

Something shook her arm. It was Bessie, trying to rouse the child's instinct for action, one to which she herself was lost. Falling on her bare knees, Janet fumbled for the poker at the edge of the tile, raised it then faltered. The cat in the fireplace, the child on the rug: their gaze met and steadied. And Janet knew she would do nothing. She had been taught to respect his privacy too well. It was Bessie who didn't see. She tore the poker from the child's flaccid fingers and lunged at the coals. The pyre split, caught the inrush of air and blazed higher. A heady, throbbing purr curled suddenly about the room as Blackie seethed, scintillated like a roman candle with the fur searing down and in till all his blackness dazzled out in reds and sparking yellow. The last of him was a flash of green eyes slatted black, a stink of scorched meat. Pork.

Bessie dropped beside the child on the rug. The purring sound had gone and the fire licked tamely in the grate while Bessie sobbed on the hearth, rocking over her knees. Janet put out a tentative hand and held it just above the woman's pulsing shoulder. They were not intimate enough to touch but Janet held her hand there, in the curving space above, till the woman raised herself to face the fire. Her cheeks were quite dry. Though her whole frame shook, there were no tears. Janet allowed herself to relax a little but never took her eyes from Bessie's face. You never knew. Seconds ticked from the mantel clock. Eventually, Bessie clenched her fists and spoke to the open box of the grate: It was what he would have wanted after all. She closed her eyes and sighed, accepting. It was settled between the three of them.

It was well after tea time the next day when the girl chose again to slip through the brown door and along Bessie's path with her arm raised to knock. It had seemed the best time: late enough for only a short visit but enough to show she remembered. She waited a moment, concentrating, before letting the tight ball of her knuckles strike. There was no answer. This was not all that unusual: Janet's knock was feeble at the best of times and Bessie was going deaf. Today, it was understandable if both gave in to their weaknesses. She moved away from the door and inched to the front-room window, the chap-shaped hand boned in to her mouth. Inside, in the usual chair, the old lady sat staring into the fireplace. It was the dull twilight time of night or day and the fire was new-built. It existed still as a tumulus of coals with the smoke streaming out between black hollows, twisting together in a spit-colour column up the chimney. The underside glittered faintly. Bessie sat deep in her chair, looking.

Janet felt sad and rubbed her fingers lightly on the glass. The old woman didn't see any more than she heard. It would be better to come back later maybe. The girl shuffled over the spongy evening grass, on and across to the wall. There was only the cemetery and a few late birds.

Janet was still looking out, counting the tombstones melting against the fog when an echo of her name from a thin mouth tapped her shoulder. Bessie was standing at the door, a furrow on the waxy yellow brow, waiting. There was something strange here: not just that Bessie should call out but also that she wasn't properly dressed. She was draped in dark, rose-coloured candlewick, held together at the waist with one fist. Her hesitation meant Bessie had to call again and wave the free hand to encourage. She didn't seem angry, just impatient, stepping aside for the child to go inside before she came after. The door closed with a dry squeak of rust.

It was stiflingly hot. The fire had been banked very high and was fully alight now, flashing seesaws onto the wallpaper. Janet stood next to her chair while the old woman faced her. There was something in her hand, held out in an envelope of fingers. It hovered over the space where Janet was expected to open, holding out for whatever was inside. She uncurled her palm and Bessie did the same. A silver-coloured ball dropped from one to the other: a split sphere with a bearing inside. A bell. Blackie's bell, cold and whole through the flames. Janet stared for a moment then raised her eyes. They watched each other and the fire crackled. The room was very still, comforting. They touched briefly. Only once.

Bessie stepped back a pace from the rug to let the rose-coloured candlewick fall. The child watched her coating of papery skin, limp about the bones and yellowed in the firelight as Bessie stepped up, raising one foot onto the tile surround and nudged the poker aside. Janet kept watching. The old lady steadied herself and breathed deep then in one gliding movement, thrust her body forward into the flames. She managed a half-smile as the child lifted the poker to help.

GOING UP AND COMING DOWN

When me and my friend Alison
were walking (late) one evening to the
top of Arthur's Seat, we met
two women
(twice our ages)
on the same path coming down.

They
(one of them was auburn-going-
grey, the other sandy-white) had
stopped for breath,
and smiled at us
(the harmless sort of smile) in much
the way that we smiled back.

Two pair of strangers, dusk and bits of
Edinburgh between.
        I thought still,
something was familiar, pushing
strands of auburn fringe (it's always
windy there) in place.
Alison (who hates to wait) just
wasn't there: the blond head fading
round the crag,
elsewhere.

It didn't really matter: and (of course)
I didn't shout.

By now,
the sandy-white was shifting
down the slope: the redhead (going grey)
like me, behind.

We moved together, chasing distant other halves
til back to back
just yards apart
we knew
and double-took.

Each turned and saw
(we knew we would)
the same blue eyes look back.

Our glances broke, embarrased:
too polite. We didn't say:
going up and coming down
(respectively)
and thirty years away.

MATERNAL INSTINCT

The male Sergeant-major fish
patrols his flock:
on sentry for the stuccoed rock
of Silent-major eggs.

Below
a fleet of congers hang some
inches south.
They gape wide-eyed and sniff perfume
of hatching Sergeant-minors.
They know it can't be long:
a second's slip is all it takes.

The male Sergeant-major fish
heroic
keeps his guard.

His Sergeant-majorette swims reefs elsewhere.
She knows he'll
cope.

Thelma Good

POEMS

GRANDMOTHER'S SAMPLERS

Only morning light is pure enough for samplers.
There she calmly sits, stitching in the symbols,
of houses, interests and milestones gained.
So we have the beauty of our lives immortalised
stitched down, by weft and warp defined,
crossing right-angled, on the right side.
Picking out the good, unpicking all the rest
the happy marriage, not the police arrest.
Granny plans, redesigns for us our pasts
showing the lie of our lives for others' eyes.
Future children will know how she saw us
stitched down still, framed when we are dust.
Through her eyes we will be consistent and strong
in sampled life histories where nothing goes wrong.

MARRIAGE LINES

Travelling by an old route
the view from the memory is embellished,
reformed and revised.
The seedling plantation has grown
to a forest
the paths obliterated.
We slow through allotments
cleared for a year's growing
and stop at a station gleaming
in its eighties red and glass.
Though the guard still blows a whistle
the bridge we slip away under
is new, prestressed concrete.
Twenty years ago it was stone and
I ran across it to a destination which wasn't.

These days I stay on the train
knowing my destination.

Anne Hay

THE LIONESS

She would have to do something about him. He was beginning to smell already. And the flies! But she couldn't move him on her own, and Sheldon wouldn't be back until tomorrow. So Elsa wrapped him in bin bags stamped 'Property of Edinburgh District Council', covered him with some trays of ice-cubes and a couple of sliced loaves from the freezer, and went next door for some fly-spray.

"Funny, I haven't got any flies," remarked Mrs Buckstone as she handed Elsa the aerosol.

"I'm making jam," said Elsa casually.

"Ooh," replied her neighbour in admiration. She didn't think young women did that sort of thing anymore. Elsa was the sort of neighbour she liked. She kept her side of the privet hedge trimmed, weeded her garden regularly, and always folded away her rotary clothes drier when not in use.

"I'm very partial to home-made jam," she called as Elsa left.

Elsa cursed to herself, and wondered whether Mrs Buckstone would be fooled by a jar of Hartley's tipped into another container. Life could get so complicated sometimes.

"I suppose you want me to get rid of him for you," her husband said, when he arrived home the next evening and discovered the malodorous bundle of blue polythene lying in the dining-room. He was Elsa's seventh victim. At first it had been a bit of a shock to Sheldon, but he had been very understanding, and he was not the sort of man who expected his wife to be just a housewife.

"Well, I can hardly put him out to the bucket."

"I don't know," said her husband, "It says 'No hot ashes' and 'No garden refuse' but nothing about dead bodies."

"Very funny," sighed his wife, "I'll help you with the digging."

"There's something I've always wanted to ask you," Sheldon said. They were back home. Elsa lay in his arms, limp with the evening's exertion, and smoked a cigarette. "It's just . . . do you . . . before you kill them, do you ever, well you know what I mean?"

His wife moved away from him suddenly and turned to look him straight in the eye.

"Sheldon, how could you think a thing like that? I'm a married woman. And there's all sorts of nasty things you can catch." She wrinkled her nose fastidiously. "No, I always finish them off well before that."

Her husband smiled down at her, reassured.

Two weeks later, the police were called to a shallow grave discovered on Corstorphine Hill. The Inspector, arriving on the scene, was met by a young, white-faced constable.

"Is it her again?" he asked.

"Looks like it, sir. The usual bite on the neck. And, er, the usual bit of him missing. We found it buried separately, inside a shoe box, a few yards away."

"It's her again." The Inspector shook his head in frustration. "Number seven."

"The Edinburgh Mutilator strikes again!" screamed the headlines. "What are the police doing to make the streets safe for our men?" demanded Lord Harry Ffoulkes-Waterstone, MP for Edinburgh West.

Men divided themselves into two distinct groups when it came to their reaction to the attacks. Some, still confident of their superior height and strength, would boast in bars of what they would do to the attacker, if she was unlucky enough to try it on them. Others, more wary, noted that the seven men already dead had been young, strong and above average height, and began to feel strangely uneasy when approached by strange women.

Elsa read the papers with amusement, as she sipped her coffee, and listened to "Morning Service" on the radio. Especially the tabloids, which described her as "an Amazon", "at least six feet tall", "a body-building expert with an excess of male hormones."

"Male hormones indeed!" she snorted, "What arrogance!"

But that arrogance, that masculine confidence, was her greatest weapon. She was five feet tall, seven and a half stone, with a long mane of blonde hair. No man was ever the slightest bit wary of her, even now. The crucial element in her attack. Surprise.

Sheldon was going away to Birmingham for five days, on business.

"Take care," Elsa said, as she handed him a Tupperware box, "that's some cold quiche and some date and walnut loaf for the train."

He looked at the box warily and hoped that it was. Elsa and her boxes!

"You take care, Elsa, you never know who's wandering about the streets." He sighed, for he knew by now what she would do while he was away. "Sometimes, you know, I wish you just did aerobics or went to Pippa Dee parties like other women."

She frowned. "I'm not other women, Sheldon, I'm me. And this is something I just have to do."

Thursday night was singles night at the "Last Drop" in the Grassmarket. Elsa sat down with her brandy and Babycham to watch the bar fill up. She surveyed the young men. She had a definite type in mind. Ever since she saw the "Eau Sauvage" advert in the Sunday Times colour supplement, she had looked for this ideal man. The advert, for men's toilet water, showed the torso of a man, his face hidden by his arms, his body tilted towards the camera to broaden his shoulders and narrow his waist, and a towel draped precariously around his loins. This image aroused her most primeval instincts. She shuddered slightly as she sipped her drink. And then she saw him. At the bar. Alone. But he wouldn't be for long. She swallowed the remains of her drink and went up to order another.

"Hello," she said, smiling at him and looking him in the eye for a few seconds.

"Hello," he smiled back, and his eyes travelled across her. She was glad she had had her hair done this afternoon, and the highlights put in it. She wore a black strapless dress, black stiletto heels, and black lacy evening gloves.

"Would you like a drink?" he asked.

"Let me get you one," she said. This was always a good ploy, and anyway, men tended to blanch when she asked for a brandy and Babycham.

"All right."

It was only after she handed him the drink that she dared to look at him. His shirt had three buttons undone. A tiny wisp of hair on his chest curled round and back onto the blue fabric. His eyes, framed by a double row of lashes, the whites made whiter by his deep tan looked deep enough to dive into and drown in. She felt a tingling sensation creep over her whole body. Her hand shook as she tried to bring the glass to her mouth. She could not tear her eyes away from his. It was a strange and inexplicable feeling she had only previously read about in books.

They danced a little, and talked a lot, and Elsa thought she'd better get him home, and do what she did with her men, before she got to like him too much. His name was Emmanuel Garth.

"Would you like to come back to my place?" she asked, stroking her hand across his thigh, in case the message was not sufficiently clear. He took her hand, placed it firmly back down beside her, and said:

"Perhaps another night."

She looked stunned.

"It's not that I don't want to," he explained, putting his arm round her fraternally, "It's just that I don't believe in casual sex. It's not just AIDS. It's . . . well, I'm attending this Assertiveness Course for Men, and we've all come to realise that we feel threatened by stereotyped male roles, which we don't want to follow. Do you understand?"

She looked blankly at him.

"If you'd like," he continued, almost as if he was doing her a favour, "you can come back to my flat, and I'll make you some Spaghetti Carbonara, and we can listen to some records."

She nodded, shocked into agreement.

As she watched his strong but sensitive hands whisk the eggs and cream and fry the bacon, she realised she had fallen in love.

"I always grate my own Parmesan," he confided in her.

"So do I!" she said, in astonishment, "but I've never met anyone else who does."

They discovered they had many other things in common: they both liked "Eastenders", the music of "Buck's Fizz" and playing "Trivial Pursuit". At three in the morning, when Elsa had filled her token with six colours, and had only one more question to answer, he looked her in the eyes and asked:

"Which comic featured 'Dan Dare'?"

She knew then she would be his.

"The Eagle," she replied, breathlessly.

They both gazed at each other for a few seconds, unwilling to break the spell.

"Would you like to do it all over again?" he hardly dared to ask, "I'm game."

"Game?" she queried, puzzled, thinking of the word in its hunting context, "Oh, I see what you mean. Yes, please."

She left his flat at ten o'clock the next morning after a night of chaste love and a breakfast of Safeway's frozen croissants. As she gaily hoovered that morning, the songs on the radio took on a new and special meaning, the world seemed a new and exciting place, its colours more vibrant, its odours and tastes more fragrant than ever she had experienced. At noon, she abandoned her duster, J-cloth and liquid Flash, and found herself drawn towards the local church, where she knelt in the back pew and prayed to be forgiven for the excesses of her past life.

"Truly," she wept, "I am born again."

She would have to tell Sheldon. He arrived home the next day, with a lecherous grin on his face, and a bundle of dirty laundry. Normally she would have considered it her wifely duty to relieve him of both, but today she could not. She struggled on for a few weeks, trying to live as before, but it was no good. She asked for a divorce. Emmanuel would not hear of her coming to live with him until they were properly married.

"Does he know about your unusual hobby?" Sheldon asked.

"I don't need that any more," she said, serenely, "Emmanuel fulfils me completely."

Sheldon went to live with a sweet, feminine, and totally reliable young nurse named Dulcie. Elsa and Emmanuel married and bought a cottage in East Lothian, with fields on three sides, and the distant sound of cows mooing.

Two years passed since the last of the "Edinburgh Mutilator" murders, and the country breathed a cautious sigh of relief.

"With any luck," the Chief Constable commented in *The Scotsman* on the second anniversary of the last killing, "this vicious and evil person has died."

One spring evening, when the clematis and cherry blossom were in full bloom, and a recent shower of rain filled the air with the sweet smell of damp earth, Emmanuel Garth arrived home to find what he thought was a man's foot sticking out of the Rayburn.

"Oh, Emmanuel!" gasped his wife, looking somewhat flushed and startled, "I didn't expect you home so soon."

A.L. Kennedy

TEA AND BISCUITS

Begin with a town in the East; the North and the East; a
Scottish town. Here, they have fogs in the morning, salty dry
and cold in the throat, that hold your breath. Some days the
mist will be gone by lunchtime. Some days you will turn down a
street and stand to see the river and a lake of white will be on it;
a milk fog, deep above the water, with nothing but the blue of a
hilltop or bare sky to show the other side. The mist nestles there,
on the cold water, hiding from the town and you; biding its time
for the other days, when it will wrap around the houses and
stay. Then you will drive through nights that are yellow, full of
glimpses of things you should recognise, things that run at you
while you squeeze along tunnels of light.

Begin with a night like that. No stars.

I went to visit him, invited, late because I had to drive slowly,
but I ran up all the stairs to make up. He opened the door and
I'll tell you what we said.

You smell the kettle boiling?

That's right.

Well, do come in.

Thank you. Thanks a lot.

The flat was very like him; in his colours, with his books, his
jacket on a chair in the living room. I recognised that. It was
warm in there; he must have been home for a while, sitting near
the fire with the paper, perhaps, and the sleeves of his shirt
rolled up.

Come and talk to me, then.

Hn?

I'll show you my kitchen. Come on.

I was wearing stockings. I like them, because they feel good,
but I thought that he would like them, too. I didn't imagine he
would see them, or that he would know I had them on, but I
thought that he would like them, if he did.

Nothing in his kitchen had names on, not even the coffee and tea. Some of it was in jars that you could see through, but for the rest you would have to remember where each thing was. Rice and porridge oats and macaroni – I didn't know then, there were ones that he always forgot.

When Michael made us coffee, he almost gave me sugar; as if he expected I'd take it because he did. In the same way, later, I would see him pick up a book and feel it was strange when he didn't put glasses on.

I noticed, back in the living room, when he bent to turn down the fire, that the grey by his temples had faded to white. The cherry light from the gas shone round his head, and the hairs that would be silver in daylight showed more red. He was no nearer balding than I remembered – hardly even thin – but his colours were changed, now. I saw that.

My grandfather was in hospital, once, a long time ago. Very ill, although nobody told me. I think he'd had a heart attack. I was taken to visit, just gran and me, and I won't forget how strange he looked. He wore new, stripey cotton pyjamas. They were something from home and didn't suit the sheets. His head was low in the pillows and I could see his throat, soft and loose where he swallowed. He wasn't like my grandfather: he was like a man. That was the time when I realised, he was a man. I kissed him goodbye and knew I was kissing a man. He must have pissed and danced and lain in bed, kissing his wife, young, and when, on special occasions, he was asked, he would always sing 'Jerusalem' because it was his favourite. Even at school. People who didn't know him wouldn't see that, they would only see how sick he was and think he might die soon. I felt guilty. I ought to have been able to love and speak to him as if he hadn't changed. I shouldn't have seen him the way a stranger would, or felt that something had let us both down.

I thought that in the morning, our waking would be something like that. Between Michael and me. I thought that I would turn and look at him and see I had wasted it all; that an ageing man I'd once admired would be sleeping, maybe snoring, at my side. He would smell of sweat. I would see the muscles in his arms were beginning to sink and be frightened by an old face, asleep, so not ashamed and weak. Slack.

I was wrong. I think, selfish, too.

The warmth of his stomach was fitted against my back and his legs behind my legs were right. Perhaps the movement had disturbed me – however it happened it was easy, and that was me awake. I answered him with a voice I hadn't heard before, my thoughts running on and feeling new, and as I turned for his arm, I didn't doubt that I could look at him safely and find good. Something good would be there. I wanted him to do the same with me.

He kissed me, I think on the nose, and said:

Good morning.

Come here. I want to tell you. I love you.

That's nice.

There are different and better ways to say it. If I'd been in America, a Russian-Jewish refugee, I could have led millions through the Dust Bowl by writing them the song about my love. I could have said that when he ran, and he often did, he ran like nobody else and I loved him for that. He had a rhythm and blues kind of run. Pale socks. I could have said I loved him for every time, but most of all for the first. That he was sweet.

Most times I would smile, or kiss him, or walk and hold his hand, because that is how people conduct themselves and some things, you don't need to say.

That morning was strange. We sat up in bed, recovering slowly, and looked at it and declared it all very odd. Herring gulls heading to sea again, flying soft and heavy up the street and a light behind the paper shop window, but no sound. The streetlamps whispered out below us and the last of the night wore away while Michael brought me tea in bed, as if I was somehow fragile, after the night.

How are you feeling?

Very nice.

You don't hurt.

No. I ache a bit.

Where.

You want me to show you?

I'm going to have trouble with you.

I told him that I'd missed the sixties, and I felt I had a lot to make up.

You missed nothing. Move over, I'm getting cold.

Perhaps what surprised us both was our luck. When I was still his student, we could have tried it; had the affair; plenty of other people always did. There were even two or three times when it could have started, like when my father died and Michael was so nice. He told me that it wouldn't get better, but I could take it a day at a time. He could have been more sympathetic and tried to get more in return. We could have let it happen then, lasted a couple of terms, maybe more. Meeting again, later, I could have been married, or he might not have had the divorce, or something very small could have happened. The day we had coffee together, one of us might have been nursing a cold, or depressed, and the chance would have gone. Instead, we had been lucky for once. For once.

All through the fogs and the drizzle, until the air became firmer and the marigolds abandoned at the close-mouth were feathered every morning with white: all through it, we learned about us. I remember how new Michael could be. I would catch him sometimes, smiling in a different light, or say goodbye to him and see him walk away and I would know there were things about him I hadn't begun to find out about yet. That pleased me.

Most of his past I knew but I couldn't share. Some of the women, I might have recognised in the street; certainly, if we'd had the chance to speak. I would have known the perfume, the way they liked to dress and, if they told me stories, I would have heard most of them before. There might be a new one, about this man with brown eyes and long hands, who liked to keep chocolate in the fridge. At the end, they would call him a bastard and look beyond my shoulder with a tired, short smile.

That was how I imagined it would be. I never had the chance to try. I never even met his wife, his ex-wife, although I wanted to. I wanted to see if she was like him in the ways that I was; to see what they had left of each other, and perhaps what would happen to us. Set my mind at rest. It might have been alright I told him. He said I was perverse, so there you go.

My past was easy. Very short. School, my school friends still in touch – enough to have a drink at Christmas, or other times, a coffee, if we met. Summer holidays and birthdays, fat-kneed boys in kilts at dances and, almost in spite of everything, no sex. Michael was surprised at that. Sometimes pleased and sometimes guilty, but always surprised at that. The University bit he knew, because he was there and because, like a few of the others, he took an interest in the people he taught. It hadn't been so long, then, since he was one of us. I had three years to fill him in on; unemployed, then selling insurance, melting down new candles for the M.S.C., and then getting the job. It took me ten minutes to tell him. The picture of me as a baby on the lopsided rug, the yellow-haired, dead father and the mother, he knew all of that.

We announced ourselves to mother, later. Like this.

It happened in the daft days. The New Year was over and the holiday nearly done, a yellow oil of lamplight over the rainy streets. We should have arrived in the Summer with light clothes and smiles; instead, our faces were numb and raw, our fingers blind with the cold. We needed to have her tea, to be comfortable by her fire, on the sofa and father's chair. By the time we had our wits about us, Mother was ready.

Go and fill the pot, will you, darling?

And away I went. I got back to find her interviewing Michael. It wasn't that we hadn't expected it, it was a natural thing for her to do, but I wish that I could have said something. Something right. Instead, I stood in the doorway, hardly listening, and thought of a book I'd found in Michael's flat. It was a hardback – Persian Art, I don't remember – and when I picked it out of the armchair to put it away, I noticed a name and address and a date on the blank leaf at the front. It told me he had lived in a different city, in a house I didn't know and he had bought himself a book, priced in shillings, when I was three years old. The nearest I can get to how I felt was, how sad it was that he would die before me. How lonely I would be. I don't think, in her interview, Mother ever mentioned that.

By the way, we hurt her. Not because of what we did, but because I hadn't told her – she hadn't known for all that time. I still saw her quite often, with Michael and alone, but always she would speak to me as if I was a guest. She didn't trust herself to me, not thoughts, or dreams, and every time I saw her, she made me ashamed.

It was almost as though she had died and, perhaps because I had lost her, or perhaps because of Michael, or both, I found that I wanted a child. I wanted to make it and have it – for it to be alive with the two of us.

My mother's pregnancy had ended very happily, laughing in fact. She had been watching a new Woody Allen film, I suppose I could find out which, and suddenly, in a silence, she laughed and found that she couldn't stop. Her laughing made her laugh. The worry in the face of my father, the usherettes, the figures who rushed her from the cinema to the ambulance; they all made her laugh. She gave birth within the hour, one month early, still weeping and giggling, amazed, and thinking of that first, secret thing which had started her laugh. I was not born even smiling, only a little underweight.

I wanted a child. I wanted it born laughing; they wouldn't be allowed to make it cry. I would tell them and Michael would make sure. I would have asked him to. I won't now.

Before the end, before I start that, there are too many things that were good, that I should remember. Sitting here, the rungs of the bench are against my spine and a crowd of sparrows is rocking a holly tree, but behind them, it is quiet. Very quiet. There is space.

I always seem to think of Michael in the kitchen – he is at his clearest, then, perhaps because we were busy together there, visiting each other, interrupting, letting things boil. I can smell the wet earth from the potatoes, our red, clay soil. He takes oranges and orangescent from a brown paper bag.

Fifty pence for five – that's not bad. They're big.

You're mean, you know that? I've noticed.

They're big oranges, look. I'm not mean.

You're stingy.

Nice, cheap oranges. I am not stingy.

You're a stingy, grouchy, old man.

He was wearing the big coat, the blue one. It smelt of evening weather and the car. I slipped my arms inside it and around his waist. That was something I did a lot.

You're just after my oranges.

That's right.

Michael stood very still for a while. He said:

You do make me happy sometimes. You don't know.

The dinner was good that day, with oranges after.

Now. This is almost the time for fog again. If I'd come to the park last week, the afternoon would have been longer, but evenings come in fast, now; you can see the change from day to day. By the time I get home, the lights will be in the windows and Michael will be back, the fires on. He doesn't like the house to be cold.

I will tell him, then, I think I will tell him.

I went there because it's a public service. In the student days, we came for the tea and biscuits, but it felt good afterwards, just the same. You knew you would have saved a life. You hadn't run into a burning building or pulled a child out of the sea, but part of you had been taken and it would help someone. I liked, then, when they laid you on the bed, with so many other people, all on beds together; something slightly nervous and peaceful in the air.

They would talk to you and find a vein, do it all so gently, and I would ask for the bag to hold, as it filled. The nurse would rest it on my stomach and I would feel the weight in it growing and the strange warmth. It was a lovely colour, too, a rich, rich, red. I told my mother about it and she laughed.

I gave them my blood a couple of times after that, then my periods made me anaemic and then I forgot. I don't know what made me go back to start again.

Nothing much had changed, only the form at the beginning which was different and longer and I lay on a bed in a bus near the shopping centre, not in a thin, wooden hall.

Afterwards, they send you a certificate. It comes in the post and you get a little book to save them in, like Co-op stamps. This time they sent me a letter instead. It was a kind, frightening letter which said I should come and see someone; there might be something wrong with my blood.

I am full of blood. My heart is there for moving blood; the pink under my fingernails is blood; I can't take it away. I am not what I thought I was. I am waiting to happen. I have a clock now, they told me that. A drunk who no longer drinks is sober, but he has a clock, because every new day might be the day that he slips. His past becomes his achievement, not his future. I have a clock like that; I look at my life backwards and behind me, it's all winding down. I think that is how it will stay. I think that's it.

Should I say to it Michael like that? Should I send him this, except that I'll throw this away? I would like to tell him the thing I remember about the American tribe. They thought we went through life on a river, all facing the stern of the boat, and only ever looked ahead in dreams.

I think he told me that – it sounds like him, but it would give me a start. I want to say it in the dark, but not in bed; I wouldn't be able to touch him that way; it wouldn't be right. I would find him in the dark and tell him when he couldn't see my face that I know he has something wrong in his blood and now I have it too.

Linda McCann

MAN AND WIFE

So now each lie takes off its mask
And leers. I made advances and you made excuses –
She wined with you and looked her best – I whined at you,
Dull as my meals. I bought my fruit in season
And my clothes out – now I window-shop
At the doorways to death, only just too low
To play ring the bell and run away.

Your key would grind in the door,
Rip me out of waiting.
I'd sink lower at the slam, wrap my pain away
In wet hankies, spread a web of silence.
Or else sometimes I'd throw up a net of questions,
Snatch at your answers, a caught-you-out catch in my voice,
Really make you shuffle your pack of lies.

But I need the faith of the colour-blind to believe it
And every dream washes me back onto the rocks.
I see you took another road a long way back –
I shout to you but the wind slaps my words
Down my throat – you smile and raise a toast to me
With my own heart. You eat it raw and make me watch –
And I just know you think it's tough, not salted enough.

One thing is true – this wife really doesn't understand you.
I have letters, diaries – made-to-measure memories
That now don't fit. A tinful of smiles,
In cities, on beaches – the camera doesn't lie –
It was as gullible as I was. Now I'm just a walking image
On a flickbook of memories. You will waken in your well-made bed
And your trail back will be moonlit, and covered by snow.

Ruth McIlroy

THE SECOND MRS ROCHESTER

Monday November 15th

Today marks a special turning-point. This morning the physician from York visited us, and he has pronounced my Edward well again!

Of course, Edward will never be the man he once was; this is something I have known since the day we were married. But he may now take some part in the everyday world again. I have decided to arrange a Christmas party for his amusement, and I have written off to dear Mary and Diana this very afternoon.

It has been a long and arduous road we have travelled together, hand in hand. When I consider the suffering he has endured, I can barely imagine what may have befallen him if I had not been here, at his side, stroking his forehead through the worst nights, cajoling him to take nourishment, teasing him back into his old spirits. "My wicked little Jane", he would call me, "my hobgoblin", and other such endearments.

My heart is proud, I confess it in this private place, at the changes I have wrought in Edward. It is sweet indeed to observe the results of my endeavours, and to know my part in his recovery. At times I could wish for a more outspoken gratitude; but Edward's is a proud nature, and I would not have him otherwise. He cannot help but know his debt to me; and that is my reward.

Tomorrow I begin to devise a programme of activities for him. The principle must be "slow and steady"; I inferred from the doctor's remarks that my rôle must now be to restrain any damaging excesses, to shield Edward from his natural impetuosity. Perhaps we shall take a walk each morning in the direction of the village, extending further every day. Then he can rest in the afternoon, while I retire here to put the final chapters to my novel. It is to be called, quite simply, *Jane Eyre*.

Friday November 19th

A beautiful autumn afternoon; but I am vexed, and cannot appreciate it. Edward has been unusually restless, and indeed has been acting in a most contradictory manner.

On Tuesday morning when I helped him dress for our first morning walk, he smiled fondly upon me, stroked my cheek and allowed me to button his boots, a task with which he is accustomed to struggle alone, in spite of his damaged hand. It is so rare that he acknowledges my little services to him; I glowed in secret for some time afterward. We passed a very quiet morning strolling in the garden, me pointing out bright objects like the holly berries which his poor eyes can now distinguish. Towards midday, I insisted that we return to the house and rest, although he wished to carry on. Later, as often in the past, we paid for the excitement with an evening of gloomy silence.

The next morning, Wednesday, he was quiet at breakfast. As we ate he informed me that today he had no need of me, and that he would walk in the company of John instead.

I concealed my hurt at a servant's company being preferred to my own, and answered him calmly that he should do as he thought best. They were away some time, and Edward seemed fatigued on his return. But when I suggested that such expeditions may prove too arduous at this early stage for one in his condition, he brushed off my concern with some remark about mollycoddling. How may I influence him? Previously, being housebound, he has followed my regime for his health, as perforce he must. Now it is become more difficult.

I know not how to interpret this new restlessness, this unheeding independence. It is best to watch, learn and say not a word. Yesterday he again walked with John, and when they returned I could swear there was a smell of drink about them. I do not care to believe that he keeps secrets.

Pray God he does not grow away from me.

Sunday 28th November

A most disturbing event has occurred, and I do not know quite how to set it down, nor in truth whether it should be set down in writing at all.

This afternoon, I was as usual at my desk, revising the penultimate chapter of the novel, in which I return to Edward and we partake of a most delicious interchange, during which I gradually reveal that it is I, Jane, come to rescue him. The pleasure I take from recounting these events quite rivals the original sensations!

I was sitting scribbling, heart beating fast, cheeks a little flushed, I dare say with the drama of it, a delightful flutter in my stomach keeping me a trifle short of breath. In walked Edward, without knocking, found his way to my desk, and in the strong afternoon light pulled me to my feet, held my face steady with his one good hand, and commenced to look at me questioningly.

I know his sight is improving, and I do not care to be examined quite so closely. Besides, I feared that he could not help but notice my state of pleasurable agitation, and I was made uneasy. Edward must not be disturbed. "Edward," said I rather sternly, "what does this interruption mean?"

"It means," said he, "that I am curious to know more of your afternoon pastimes, little Jane"; and he forthwith took to leafing through my manuscript.

"Read this out to me, Jane," he said after a while. "My eyes cannot make out the script."

I confess I felt yet more uneasy at this direction, Edward knowing nothing of the novel as yet; but then the story set down therein was true, familiar, and did no discredit to either of us. So I settled him down in an easy chair, sat down at his feet and commenced reading the chapter, at first hesitantly but then more confident as the scene unfolded. The words were working their familiar spell for me. As I reached the point of revelation, I looked up at Edward.

His face was black as thunder. "So this is the man you wish to make me," he got out as if something were choking him. His tone made me flinch, but he pulled me closer. "Fantasy!" he said harshly, right into my face. I could not understand him, nor his anger. And then, I do not know what possessed him to act so violently, he pulled me up roughly onto his knee and held me against him. "Let me kiss you, Jane, let me touch you," he said, "This is the reality of it," and then he commenced on such indignities as make my cheeks burn to remember.

How could I have been prepared for this? Where was the tenderness, the consideration for my years, my inexperience? I shudder now at the thought of his very hands. When he left I fell to weeping in chagrin and shame for him. I have made many allowances, but must I bear this?

This is not how it was intended to be. It is too soon; it is wrong; I am not ready. He must surely grant me this, after all I have done for him.

Friday 10th December

Edward made another advance upon me yesterday; this time I was prepared. Calmer reflection has convinced me that he must be forgiven his strange coarseness; after all, he may be excused for wishing to claim his natural rights before his health can withstand it. But his shameful behaviour on Sunday belittles him. I explained my feeling haltingly and with modesty; mentioned my youth and his health; and appealed to him for restraint. Mercifully, he respects my wishes. He begged my pardon and made me promise not to hate him for it; he confessed he fears losing me above anything. It was an affecting sight, and my heart went out to him again. Matters between us are thankfully much improved.

If I could only devise some way to curtail the daily walks with John, which I am convinced do Edward's moods no good, then I would be content.

For the time being, I have set aside the final chapters of the novel, the savour having gone from the writing of it. I now spend the afternoons stitching by the fire while Edward dozes. Preparations are well in hand for the Christmas gathering, and I am looking forward to the company of my two dearest friends.

I am training young Martha in the duties of a ladies' maid, so that Maria and Diana need not feel the privations of this place so greatly.

Wednesday 15th December

He has encroached upon my dignity, in my own home; it is intolerable.

This morning I walked into the drawing room and came upon Edward, laughing rudely, holding above his head a little ornamental figurine, just out of the reach of Martha, who was hanging onto his arm, giggling and crying "Please sir, don't be so provoking sir," and making a silly play of reaching for it with her duster. At my entrance both parties looked exceedingly foolish, as well they might. Martha retreated from the room in confusion. Edward flung the ornament down on a chair and came over frowning, but I left the room. I did not know what to say.

Edward has reproached me for making too much of the incident, and he may be correct. Why should he not indulge in some innocent amusement; it may even speed his recovery. But for my own reasons I find this incident disturbing. Why must he go to the maid for entertainment? Heaven can witness I know my failings. I have not been blessed with a light-hearted and merry disposition; my history has been too hard for levity, and I fancy my nature too profound. But sometimes I sense that Edward looks for more superficial qualities in me.

Why can he not accept me for myself, as I accept him with all his tempers and failings? In God's mercy, I begin to feel more than ever at a loss what to do.

I am convinced that I must counteract these recent manifestations which make Edward day by day less amenable. He has become on occasion foul-tempered; at times it is as if he is making to strike me; and yet at other times, he becomes like a little child, holding my hand and asking for forgiveness for his tantrums. I must remain calm, and seek advice. He needs now more than ever my good sense.

Saturday 18th December

I have visited Edward's physician, on the pretext of a trip to purchase a Christmas gown. I described as best I could those symptoms which have persuaded me that Edward is in need of a remedy which, alas, has proved beyond my power to devise. At the cost of some modesty I hinted at his particular appetite, and said that I knew what damage this may cause to a fragile constitution. I then begged the doctor to advise me on the correct course of management I should take to help Edward regain his former composure.

The physician sat for some minutes regarding me, at which as usual I dropped my eyes in some confusion. At length he said:

"Mrs Rochester, you will forgive me for speaking frankly. These manifestations you describe are nothing more than the natural inclinations of a full-blooded gentleman, such as I have always known your husband to be, returning to his powers. You must accustom yourself to acknowledging his will; you have ceased to be the nursemaid now, you see."

The doctor did not fully understand my situation, or he would not have been so cruel. I have not a minute to myself these days but that Edward is calling upon me in temper or in fond supplication. Or he will spend full evenings together in the servant's hall with John, where I suspect the cards and the ale come out. I cannot feel that this is how matters should be between husband and wife.

However, I am resolved no longer to refuse him, but to meet him with a tenderness and a modesty which he cannot but reciprocate.

Sunday 19th December

Edward informed me this morning that he has invited three of his former hunting acquaintances to our Christmas house-party, and bade me make rooms ready for them. I asked how we would entertain these gentlemen, who I fear are accustomed to sur-roundings more lively than our quiet retreat. He looked at me rather dryly. "You must do your best, Jane," he said, "It lies within your sphere, you know, to make us a jolly company."

"But you know I am no match for your fashionable friends," I rejoined. "I will fail, and then you will reproach me"; then I burst out in a passion, "You knew my character when you married me! We were to retire from society! Why do you ask this of me?"

"And you too, Jane, knew how I was," he paused and said with emphasis, "how I used to be – before the accident – when you accepted me. Here he stands; you have the full Edward Rochester, like him or nay"; and he grimaced, "You will have to learn how to get on with him, little Jane."

He took a step towards me, putting out his arm with a look almost pleading, and with a determination which made me retreat a little. He caught me anyway, and I was crushed half-reluctantly against his chest. I was determined not to resist; stayed still for a while; then thankfully he let me go of his own accord.

Since then, I have been shut up in here, attempting to complete the final chapter of my novel. What should I write, if I were to set down the unvarnished truth? Edward has become rough and inconsiderate? But this has been his character all along, and he has never attempted to conceal it; indeed, his harsh ways were once a great attraction. Or should I write: I have tried to change him, to make him better; and I have failed.

My love has not been strong enough to prevail. Or rather; if this is what being a wife is, I do not relish it.

I will complete the novel over Christmas.

I have written to postpone Diana and Maria's visit. There are not rooms enough for them and my husband's guests; and besides, he calls them my milk-and-water companions.

Friday 31st December

It is New Year's Eve, and I have retired here to escape. The company has departed at last. I fear that the house-party was not a great success; I am but little used to playing the hostess, and have not the arts of pleasing conversation. Edward grew steadily more dissatisfied with me as the days went by, enjoining me to cease my stiff manner and fulfil my proper duties. How does he not understand that society ways cannot come naturally to a poor orphan. I fear he does not know me well.

In truth, Edward became drunk on most evenings, encouraged by his companions. On Christmas night, the men sat up late, drinking, singing and playing poker. I shudder to recall the sight of my Edward, incoherent through brandy, peering at his cards, making a pathetic show at telling one number from another; then forcing me to sit beside him and whisper his cards into his ear as the other gentlemen sat laughing; then cursing his poor damaged limb; and finally falling in a stupor upon the carpet.

I have heard that this is the manner in which many fine gentlemen make merry; I am despairing beyond words to discover that Edward does not distinguish himself from his wilder companions in this.

I pray that matters may not become worse; yet I fear his intemperance.

Saturday 1st January

Edward came in upon me last night as I was writing, and said that he had a New Year's present for his little Jane. Leaving a parcel on the bed, he retired, saying that he would return shortly.

I opened the parcel in curiosity and trepidation. Inside was a set of engravings; but engravings such as I have never seen the like of before and hope most fervently never to see again. The licentious and shocking scenes depicted on those plates made my whole frame shake with indignation at Edward's depravity and fear of his intentions. I dropped the engravings into a corner and wiped my hands where I had touched them. Never would I submit to such coarseness; I prayed to God, and felt sure He would protect me.

When Edward came back into the room, I was at the window, silent, and he seemed to falter at my look. "I have offended you then," he said, "but you must know these things, Jane; I will not wait any longer"; and taking my arm, he drew me over to the bed. In truth, I was half out of my wits with shame and fear. Edward lay me down; I did not dare resist; but he was hurting me.

I could not help myself, but let out a cry of fear and pushed him away. "Do I disgust you so much, does this disgust you so much?" he threw at me like a madman, brandishing his damaged arm in my face. "If this is how you receive me, Jane – if you cannot be a good wife to me – then I know where else I will find comfort," he cried, or some such manner of words; and casting me aside so that I gathered up the engravings and ran out of the room.

I hardly dare speculate where he went; I do not care, in truth. Such a beast may do as he pleases.

Sunday 2nd January

I have found a little corner in this long low room in the upper reaches of the house, where I have had John fetch my bed, my wardrobe and my writing, all the while trembling that Edward would find me out and drag me back. Now that I am here, I do not think he will trouble me, so long as I do not trouble him.

I have finished the final chapter of the novel. In it, Edward and I are blessed with ten long years of married happiness, and a little baby boy; Edward's sight returns; and he loves me forever.

God knows what will become of me.

Rosemary Mackay

THE WEDDING DAY

So, there I was, sat in the tin tub, in the middle of the bedroom floor, feeling the water going cold, staring at the goose pimples on my thighs. I was sat bolt upright, in one of the two possible positions, and my bent-up knees were a hair's breadth from the tip of my nose. In that position there was no problem about where the soap was: the only space was behind my ankles, next to my bum. I thought about asking my mother to come and wash my back, decided that the odds were not in my favour and manoeuvred my feet out of the bath and onto the linoleum. From there I eased my bum forward, careful to avoid contact with the base grit which ripped soft flesh. Very gently and slowly, keeping firmly in mind the handle of the tub which jutted from the rim, I leant back until the top of my spine was touching the inside of the tub and my chin was wedged on my chest. Now the soap had to be in the triangle between spine and tub, unreachable.

I eyed the scum which was lapping around my crevices, and reckoned that with my back done, my conscience was clear. That made two baths in one week. Would Lizzie do the same for my wedding, I asked myself. The front door of our flat opened and I heard my sisters' laughter as they went into the living room. They had time to go to the Public Baths but my paper-round stopped me. Heaven and earth might pass away but that bloody paper-round would go on and on. I sighed, heard myself sighing, and began the business of drawing my body into an upright position. My feet, still on the linoleum, were freezing.

It was a farce, the whole bloody business. Here was Lizzie, saving all her earnings for two whole years to pay for the White Wedding, Cathedral Service with Nuptial Mass, the big Reception in the best Hotel in town, and every relative we possessed, who had not spoken to any of us in years and would not speak again after today, invited to attend. They would be there: they couldn't resist the temptation of the gilt-edged Invitation Card. But they were coming in the hope of catching us out, we, the lower-class branch of the family.

And the fiancé. Well, my God, wasn't he a corker. Hamish, who spoke through a mouthful of marbles, and could be seen, his neighbours had said, sporting the old school tie as he dug his patch. Certainly, he had never crossed our threshold: all social niceties had been performed in the lobby, no matter the time of day or temperature. I had amused myself speculating on how to get Hamish out to the back garden where he could be invited to "avail himself of our facilities." But Lizzie roused had a hell of a punch on her and could kick like a kangaroo.

I towel-dried the goose pimples away, deciding that I would put on the new underclothes now, but I'd be damned if I was going to wear that dress before it was absolutely necessary. Not that you could hope to stand on principle in a farce. That had been made quite clear when Mother started acting up in the shoe shop. Which had nothing to do with anything I had said: she was just overwrought by her own finer feelings. That and the heat, and the quarrelling and the dirty looks we were getting from the shop assistant.

But there was still two hours till the show got on the road, and dressed in that crazy rig-out, I would not be able to do the fetching and carrying, accept my "delegated responsibilities", as Lizzie called them. She would persist in treating me as though I was as gullible as the rest, though you could tell sometimes from her face that she wasn't getting the same satisfaction, the cheeky bitch. I pulled on my dirty jeans and went to meet what had to be the last in a life-time of tantrums from my older sister.

Lizzie was standing in the middle of the living room floor, arms aloft, supporting umpteen rolls of white material, face livid as she hissed at her sisters: "Get a hold on either side, you gormless buggers. It weighs a ton." I had never before been favoured with a full frontal of my sister, even half-clothed, since we all four always got ourselves into contortions trying to avoid the casual glance as we wrestled into pyjamas, bras, knickers. Life was simpler in behind the clothes-horse, but when the drier was up there was no room for anyone else to move. Now, as the descending hemline concealed, first, a scattering of plooks, then the chalk-white midriff, next the sprouting pubic hair and finally a small ladder in one stocking, I recognised that cover had its advantages.

"What are you gawping at? And what the hell kept you? Get the zip." It was a beautiful dress, I had to admit it. But I couldn't understand why it was going on now, with the rollers and naked face above it. I knew I could rely on one of my sisters to do the necessary: "Why are you putting it on now, Lizzie?" asked wee Jessie.

"Why the hell do you think? Get a hold of the train, carefully. And get a chair. I'm wanting to have a look."

In procession we moved slowly to the positioned chair, which Lizzie gingerly mounted. The mirror, which was eight inches by eight inches, reflected Lizzie's splendidly-clad stomach.

"Hold the train back," she said and slowly began to bend her knees until she could see her own neckline. Then, centimetre by centimetre, she straightened her knees until she could see her stomach again. Now, she went on tip-toe, craning up until she got a view at knee height: "Jesus, this is just a bloody game."

"My sentiments, exactly," I offered, and received a stinging slap on the side of my head.

"And who bloody asked you?" she said. I gave her one of my winning smiles and wondered where on earth Mother had gone.

Lizzie stepped off the chair, and the train was placed at her ankles. "Get me something to protect the dress. A tea-cloth or something to catch the powder. And for God's sake start getting ready. Jessie, Ellen. Move it."

I draped a tablecloth round her shoulders, pinning it at the back: "Anything else?" I said. "Where's your make-up?" I knew she would do a great job on her face. Any night of the week she could swan out of here looking like one of the jet-set.

"I'm fine. See to yourself, Mary."

She tossed a powder compact at me which I took to be for my personal use. In the mirror of this contraption you could see two whole square inches of your face at a time. I propped it against the milk jug and sat down at the table.

The door opened and mother came in with her coat and head-square on: "Uncle Jimmy wasn't in, but Auntie Maisie says everything is under control, and he'll be here at twelve."

"Oh, where's he then? Down at the pub?"

I threw mother's flushed face a glance and she shook her head vigorously at me. "Oh Jesus," I thought. "That's all we're needing."

"How's he getting here?" asked Lizzie.

"They've got a taxi ordered." Presumably in case he couldn't walk. Mother disappeared into the bedroom carrying a basin of hot water. She had no time now for an all-over effort.

I concentrated on my right eye, pulling the eye-liner pencil as firmly as I could across the puckering flesh. For years I had watched Lizzie do this with the total concentration of an artist. And though I could applaud her finished efforts, I remained unconvinced where my own mask was concerned. What, after all, was it for? The outside world, as far as I knew, was unmoved by my efforts. I spat into the cracked cake of mascara, and rubbed the clogged, solid bristles of my brush, spittle-covered, on the black, resisting block. I had tried to stand my ground on this issue too, sidling past the waiting Lizzie in my Sunday clothes, barefaced but scrubbed clean. The sneer she gave me then, had me reaching for the make-up bag before I had time to register a change of mind.

I opened my eye as wide as possible and with trembling hand, waved the loaded brush at my flickering eyelashes. The roar which came from the bedroom sent the brush flying across the table, and my body into collision with Lizzie's in the doorway.

"Jesus God. Jesus, help me."

My mother was lying on her back across the bed, breasts and open mouth reaching for the ceiling, her vast corset packed tight. She was waving her arms and a loud sob escaped from her throat.

"What the hell is it?" Lizzie stood over her, staring down at the purpling face. My mother's left hand made an arc and her fingers began to scrabble at the reinforced cotton of her corset. It was done up to midway and then gaped obscenely at her navel. Beneath this I noticed tiny mounds of blue flesh poking through at the join: she was trapped.

At that moment, Lizzie flung the tablecloth from around her neck and began to force open the hooks and eyes which trapped the purple bumps. My mother let out a scream and pulled her knees up towards her belly. It was then that I saw the cord which was laced to draw the front of the corset together.

"A pair of scissors," I said as I rushed to the sideboard drawer. There was everything but.

"A knife," I said. Mother's screams were making my stomach cramp. I knew the carver was as blunt as a spade and so I whipped up the breadknife. Back in the bedroom, I began to saw at the cord, glad that I had something to do, trying to shut out the now white face, the dying sobs. When the last thread snapped, my mother's arched torso slumped. Lizzie unhooked the lumps and my mother let out a final groan.

"And that had better be the last thing I ever do in this bloody madhouse. Mary. My train." Lizzie snatched up her tablecloth and, in procession, we left the bedroom.

And then we had to go; me, Mother, Jessie and Ellen in one taxi, and Uncle Jimmy, in striped trousers and tails, weaving in the doorway, his nose already a bluish-purple. Lizzie, majestic in veil, had taken one look at his leering face and swept past him into the bedroom, Ellen pursuing the flicking train.

"Aye, it's good to see you, James. You're looking very nice." My Mother always treated drunks with patient good humour, and I could never see the point. "Aye, the girls are looking lovely," she responded to his grin at me and Jessie. "We're away now. You and Lizzie's tazi will be in five minutes. Take care."

"My God, could he not have just this once laid off . . ."

Our own father had gone off on a binge four years ago and hadn't been seen since. So, Jimmy, mother's brother, stood in when necessary.

"Now don't go on, Mary," said Mother. "He's just behaving the way he always does for weddings."

"But he's giving her away, for God's sake. He'll be staggering down the aisle."

"Don't underestimate him, Mary. He's had plenty of practice. And don't go on. Is my flower straight?"

She patted the spray above her left breast. "I think they've made a lovely job of the flowers, don't you?" She stroked her stomach and winced.

Now that we were away from the house, my younger sisters were exploding with laughter next to my mother. "Calm down, you two. You're flower-girls. Behave like it."

I sat in the front seat, clutching a pink posy, desperate at the thought that I couldn't expect a fag until the Reception. Then I remembered my mother's handbag: "Light a fag, Mother, I'm gasping."

"You can't, Mary. Not dressed like that."

"Look Mother, if Uncle Jimmy can turn up pissed out of his brains, then I can smoke a fag."

"Ssh," she said with a headjerk at the taxi driver, who showed an impassive profile. She lit the cigarette, taking three quick draws on it, in her infuriating way, and passed it to me.

Mother went in to take her seat, and we stood in the Church

vestibule waiting for Lizzie, from where I could see the seated congregation, resplendent in fur stoles and huge hats. And we hadn't even had an autumn frost yet. Suddenly Mother burst through the glass doors, her eyes frantic: "He's not here. God Almighty. He hasn't turned up." She was trying to whisper, but seemed to have little control of her voice.

"Who, the Minister?"

"No. That bloody Hamish!" Mother had, to date, spoken of him only in neutral terms.

"Well, she's not here either."

"But he's supposed to be. Dear God, what if he's jilted her?"

And what if he had? Wouldn't that be the last laugh for the guests. "The McIvies have done it again. Another glorious cock-up." I could hear them all at it. Not that we ever had done the like before. But it was easy to establish a tradition in inferiority, if the will was there. I'd kill him if he had let us down.

Mother pulled her head back in the front door: "Lizzie's here. I'll have to go and tell her. They'll hold everything for a while." She disappeared again, and I became conscious of the sweat gathering in my armpits. My little sisters looked stricken.

"Come on," I said. "It could be the best thing that's happened to her."

"But I'm affronted," said Ellen, and her lower lip began to wobble.

"Don't you dare greet," I said. I wanted to go into the pulpit, mount a machine gun, and mow the congregation down.

Through the glass doors, I could see heads slowly turning, then moving together for whispered messages. Feet were beginning to shuffle. "It's all right, you'll get your bloody presents back," I wanted to scream. Instead, I moved to the door and opened it.

Mother was tripping across the street, knees pushing her dress forward, hat slightly askew. Behind her, I could see Lizzie's taxi. Even Uncle Jimmy's face seemed to have gone a few shades paler. Lizzie shouldn't have to take this. I felt a surge of loyalty and pity that almost choked me.

And then, there he was. With a great roaring of engine and screeching of brakes, he leapt out of the roofless sports car, and loped towards me, a flop of blonde hair across one eye.

"Where the hell have you been?"

His best man burst in behind him and my words were lost. Within minutes they had struck up 'Here Comes the Bride', and for one terrifying moment, I thought I was going to let the side down and shed a tear.

Lindsay McKrell

POEMS

I have this dream about a schoolboy
Hesitant and sensual
delicate and vulnerable
on the threshold of it all
No awkward, spotty, sweaty schoolboy
But the sort who is tall, who is seventeen
Clear-skinned and open-featured
The nape of whose neck demands to be kissed
He sits himself slyly in front of me
Daring me to do it.
Oh get thee behind me Satan
This succulent specimen
Was not meant for me
But even the temptation
Sends my senses reeling
And the sweetest sensation
Is just breathing him in
And thinking what might come to pass
If sensibility deserted me
And I got reckless.

BREAKING UP

This boy, the ordinary boy,
Is a thin freckled specimen, old and serious,
Wide eyes set in a funny face.
Baggy shorts, socks grubby,
Shoes his mother's given up polishing.
He heads his feet out of the school gate,
Jumps cracks on the pavements.
His satchel hangs from his hand,
Scrapes at his side.
He's on his own again,
He's late out tonight,
The January dark masses.

He doesn't walk with his head up
Or talk much
He doesn't brag
He'll never be a leader.

He watches the moon
Zooms off on a private flight of fantasy
Nestles in cloud.
Whispers, scuffling footsteps break in behind,
He wheels round, curious,
To catch all the boys in his class,
And the first fist in his face!

He stumbles,
The world flips over.
The bruises of black branches on indigo night sky
Bump and graze.
A slow incomprehensible moment
Leaves him numb and fumbling.
The ground hits him
A brutal body blow.
Kicks follow.
Spluttered shouts of, "Get him! Bastard!"

Fist and foot thud against this cringeing boy,
Disbelieving.
He feels no pain

Just the thud and the scrape
Of boots on road
And his own mouth whimpering in a foreign tongue.
A ring of snarling faces loom,
Eyes steely, greedy and unrecognisable
The whole world's turned black and blue

Too shattered to fight
He waits it out
Their swearing in his ears
And the scrapes of the kicks
That time won't silence . . .

When the last fist crunches
An army of feet scamper out of view
He watches the sky throb less angrily
Staggers,
Scoops up his scattered books, pens, jotters, string,
Wipes his bloodied nose on his school jumper
His dad'll kill him.
Getting blamed for being victim.
There is no actual pain yet
But he dreads shuffling home,
Head hung.
Most of all facing them next morning
Facing up to loneliness again.

Being beaten up was chickenfeed,
Because he senses deeply what no one else will guess,
    That he will grow up,
    He will run,
    He will flinch,
    He will blubber,
And when all of that is over,
With each bruise gone,

Each scab picked,
This ordinary boy in scuffed shoes,
Heading home under orange streetlights,
Could end up scarred for life.

THE SAME OLD SCENE

It's cold in here
Look, you can see my breath in little clouds
Even though the heater's been on hours
Calculating its Easter surprise
Which will probably be prompter
Than the phonecall I'm waiting for, staying in for,
Same old story.
Half of me knows, even as my eyes steal a sneaky glance
at the phone sitting smugly beside me, keeping me company,
That it never will ring
It will maintain its stubborn silence
Teaching me a lesson again
Well that's okay I suppose
I should have known better
But I'd made such plans,
Notified friends and neighbours of my new status
Part of a couple again
More of a whole
Than I can be on my own
And I was going to dress up, go out, get drunk,
dance and sing and laugh uproariously,
Like I haven't done in such a long time
Like I've just about forgotten how.

Well it doesn't matter really
It's just I hadn't met eyes that warm in ages
Felt so companionable with a stranger
Felt the first tinglings of an unfamiliar lust
I thought had extinguished itself
For my own safety.
It probably will do now.

I understand I might not fit in to other people's plans
I'm not the sort of girl that ought to be
sitting here, doing this, for the nth time
Like it was my hobby
It's not a thing you need much practice at
and I'm getting to be something of an expert.

I'm too independent for this
Too busy, I have better things to do
It's just that I have found the sweetest pleasures
with men, have felt the best and worst of emotions
most keenly in their company, I've seen them as
the key to contentment and knowledge of myself
Wrong though it may be.

And it's my fault I've expected too much again
Because waiting for phonecalls, waiting for men
Is no way to live your life
And I know if I really try, I can find those same
sweet pleasures in friends and in myself.
If I'm scared of being on my own
If I still yearn for some man
To tell me I am pretty or clever or funny or kind
Then that will pass, as they do
I can be alone
Or go out with friends
It is quite possible to have fun that way
To paint the town red
Without having to impress anyone
Unselfconscious
Riotous
Vulgar and silly and unrestrained
Good times again, I feel fine in this
treacherously thin new skin,
with my phone number
Classified information.

Maureen Macnaughtan

POEMS

SINGAPORE DAYS
(Joss-sticks)

In the land of orchids
getting a work-permit
is harder
than hatching a phoenix.

Sooner or later opportunity shines on inertia.
Rooted in small gifts –
quartered in narrow rooms
your clouds explode
with the wisdom of the Dragon.

Every fibre is alive
you walk with the Gods,
but what was spontaneous
keeps the ladder hidden.
After the ashes – it takes
more than a joss-stick
to chase the demons away.

PROLONGED EXILE

There's nothing to catch
when you lip-read.
Being an audience for one
makes the players elucidate,
mouths twist & flap like goldfish.
If the mind wanders
they won't begin again,
the gestures become smaller
till the neck – guillotines down.

The deaf always miss the punch-line.
They are prisoners in a jungle
of silhouettes & roaring lions.
Worst are the contortionists,
sometimes I long to hold
a mirror – show the bewildered
HOW to candle the silence.

Angela McSeveney

POEMS

'OH, I'M UNEMPLOYED.'

That phrase just erased me.
Her reply falls flat.

She daren't ask me if I enjoy it
nor suggest that it must be fun.

I feel like a bluebottle in the ointment.
She brought no prearranged pigeonholes
which can take me.

All she knows is that I do nothing.

"What would you like to do?" she tries,
to fill in my wavering outline.

UNEMPLOYED

When the door slams for the fourth time
my hasty goodbye hangs unheard
at the ceiling.

That last pair of feet is running late
to a nine o'clock deadline.

I too rose early:
"How did your day go?" dares me
to have an unrehearsed reply.

I annoy myself by feeling abused
when I agree to wait in for tradesmen.

I eat lunch alone
staring at the draining board.

As I rinse my cup and plate
the unwashed breakfast dishes watch me.

Perhaps mothers feel like this, minimising the mess
with yesterday's cold vegetables.

A HIRSUTE WOMAN

A friend first mentioned it, not quite
behind her back.

When she filched her father's razor
the bathroom felt as cold
as her dread of discovery.

In Summer she wears long sleeves
and dark tights.

Sometimes she swims alone
and imagines that the flattened hair
looks like fur.

SCABIES

When I became one huge burning itch
I rubbed and chewed and bit
till there was blood on the bedsheets.

I gnawed my hands at night
worrying between the fingers.

Our GP said my skin eruptions ran
in the family and prescribed
something for eczema.

Patiently Mum rubbed the stuff
into my most tender folded places.
The chemist suggested an old-fashioned remedy.

The bottle was made of thick brown glass
with fluted edges.

Each night I screamed it burned
and begged her to stop.

It tasted bad
so I couldn't chew my fingers.

I slept better then,
its stickiness gluing the pyjamas
to my heated skin.

LATE PERIOD

We just drank coffee and talked.

You rubbed my stomach
till acrylic blue sparks crackled off my jersey
then you joked that something kicked you.

There was one day left
till we'd know if I was reprieved.

When we kissed goodbye at the top of the stairwell
I heard the smack echo in the high glazed ceiling.
"I'm sure it'll be okay."

Earlier that day I'd paced across the Meadows
trying to shake my stomach free of that tight feeling
– cramps, I was sure, like any other month.

I lay down to bed,
my eyes dry with tiredness.

With you gone, the toy bear beside me
wouldn't give any comfort.

Six am: I need to pee.
The light bleaches my face grey
as it hangs in the mirror.

I put a foot on the bath edge
to open myself with my fingers
and search for flecks of blood.

COMING OUT WITH IT

You couldn't know that I wanted you,
so you chose your moment carefully.
I froze.

I took some time to react,
trying to be tactful.

You were frozen too
in my five second pause.

There was sense in your caution.

Of course I was shocked when you told me
about shouts in the street
and your sister's reaction.
I wouldn't reject you.

But even now, for a moment,
homosexual stops being a trait.
It rears up, a title.

I blink it away.
You settle into focus.

You say that when you told me
I stopped stroking your hand.

I smile because you still can't measure
the meaning of caresses given by a girl.

Janet Paisley

POEMS

MATTHEW

I wish, he says

making the word with his wet full mouth,
his eyes round beacons of delight
at all the words he can wish into life.
Small wide hands expand the sound
and draw the bigness of his wishes in the air,
he is all eagerness,
a colt quivering muscled shoulder at the taste of wind,
and belief's disciple
as hands of expectation clap in trust.
He just has to say and it is there.

A conjuror he is, no game
this magic he makes is getting
tongue and teeth and lips
to name his dream.

ALIEN CROP

So the boats come in
charcoal shadows etched on liquid gold –
she is not always so fine a mistress
her depths combed smooth with light.
I have waited through nights
of her grey lady, webbed with mist,
while she whispered her possession
on the bloodless stone. I have watched
her raking claws rise, a green harlot
shrieking spit, jealously making
her grave bed ready below the heaving sheets.
This dusk is still and holds the cat-purr
of engine and the call of voices,
clear on shore as if an echo sounded near.
You will come, a stranger dying in your eyes,
the man I have never known, tasting of tears,
salt fingerings in your hair,
her blood-kisses whitening on your mouth.
I know only your feet at the fireside,
your hungers and your tossing sleep,
the wearing of you and the leavings.
It has been a long standing between us,
these dry shore waits but now, on this late tide
I feel the child-swell within me.
I still wait your landfall, the wet
song of rope, the scrape of wood, the alien
crop of you, and know a new strangeness
for I too am fishing
in the drift of a setting sun.

RIDE WITH THE HUNTERS

I have hidden from elephants
in this small Scottish village,
remembering to bolt the doors
of this thicket where I live.

I had forgotten that bricks crumple
like petals from a poppy flower
and wood splinters with as much resistance
as prairie grass under those leaden feet.

Try supplicating an elephant.
It's water off a mud bank to a raging bull
and in their quiet basking
merely makes them flap their ears.

So now I ride with the hunters,
having cut my teeth on that same wood
and honed sharp talons upon mortar
while clawing my way out.

I have swooped down with the bats
and taken the eagles flight
beyond their reach. I learned from wolves
to slaver blood and spittle in the night.

And I can draw blood –
and I can bay at the moon.
And I don't fear elephants any longer,
only my own ferocity.

Joy Pitman

LUMB BANK COLLAGE

All trees and water and light on leaf and water on branch and grass and you in the grass and the ferns, the window out of the barn onto green, sky and leaves in puddles, deep hanging primeval branches over secret paths, water flowing, bark peeling and cracking with its own slow-motion flow.

Green. Water. Light.

I want to sit absorbing the stone beneath me, the sound of distant water, birds crowing, flies humming, sun warming, breeze on the back of my neck. Or become an insect walking through forests of grass, tall, bending over me, the sun drifting down, bars of light and dark and light against the earth, crumbs of earth as huge as footballs, a worm gliding and shining, its circles contracting and expanding, pushing the earth through its body, patient.

Light through the chinks in the wall, low, old, weathered, placed stone carefully on selected stone, the flowers clinging tenaciously in the crevices, pale purple sparks of life, the lichens spreading in slow puddles on its surface, soft furred moss, drying ferns. A wall for the sun to shine on, a line between the path and the meadow, marking the way.

Green green green. Everywhere green. Light on green, light behind green, light through green. Insisting, pushing at me, forcing me to take it in.

And water. Drops on the grass reflecting the sun, mist in the air hazing the distant green valley, furrowed up through the curling trees, moistly inviting. I can feel your contours with my eyes, I want to plunge my hand between your coyly spreading legs, drink the stream which runs down from your misted hills.

101

The rain. The rain, the blessed sweet wet rain. How I need the rain. Tense dry electric head-aching anxious waiting for the rain, the stifling before-storm anticipation, air heavy, pregnant, morose, clouds grumpy with unfulfilled expectation. I can feel the clouds over my bent back and the heavy drops waiting to fall. They would fall hard and insistent and welcome and soak me through and through and wash all the old pain away. I want to be baptised by the thunderstorm, the wave that drowns me, the downpour that soaks right through, into my skin, forcing itself into my bloodstream, my guts, my liver, my spongey lungs soaking up the oxygen.

Oh the thunder, the crash and rumble of it, the electricity charging the sky, discharging from the air across the valley. The wonderful might power and sheer unashamed noise of it, breathing freely again. And the pouring voluptuous drenching and soaking unending downflow of the rain. Drumming on the earth, the tree-tops, sliding down windows, licking the leaves and dripping drop by drop to roll down the valley of the vein of the leaf below. And the river joyful and laughing with the gush and flow of the rain running from the hills down its valley, water over the stones, white drops flying, the rush under the hovering leaves, roots and stems of growing water plants, green weed streaming in the current like hair in the wind. The water loves the stony bank, the ledges, the furrows, caresses the hard stone, smoothes it, leaps laughing over the ridges, dances beneath the hanging ferns.

I could have laid you down in the wet leaves and kissed your open mouth and licked the raindrops from your cheeks. I could have spread my jacket over us with the rain drumming on to it and we could have been warm beneath the trees. I want to take you in the open air, among the bluebells and the ferns, blue and green, green and blue. I want to pour my love over you, wash you with caresses like a fine rinsing rain. I want you to smile back at me, gentle me, cradle me, comfort me, bring me back to bliss again and again and again. Then roll over and over down the hillside through the bracken one round bundle of limbs and legs hugging laughing. I want to take you outside in the sunshine and the night-time and the fire time and the rain.

And afterwards the air clear and sweet, the earth singing and sucking and drinking and breathing back rich fruity odours, rivulets beside the stones, puddles in the grass, drops standing reflecting the whole world and refracting the light of the sky on a blade of grass, drops dripping from the spikey ends of sedges into the dark peaty pool, gentle ripples echoing out, criss-crossing, enmeshing. And here in the black hollow of an overhang beside the track, a spider's web laced with crystals of moisture: a circlet of diamonds round a circlet of diamonds round a centre shimmering with light.

Green. Water. Light.

Dilys Rose

DRIFTER

Fiona had kept moving west in the hope that home ties would stretch and thin out like rubber bands until they snapped, leaving her free to hang loose in the new country, on the temperate shores of the Pacific. At times, homesickness stopped her in her tracks – flashes of dark tenements blotting out a sunny Canadian day, monochrome shots of Glasgow, Scotland, in her mind's eye, a hungry beast of a city, crouched over the wide dirty Clyde. Voices, accents from home, unchanged after decades, heard at bus terminals, in the stacked aisles of supermarkets, they could be ignored. The Scots were all over Canada. It was at other times, when she was least expecting it, least prepared, that homesickness washed over her like a wave and then she wanted nothing except to be swept on through eight hours of Greenwich Mean Time, back to the city from which she had escaped.

That was what she'd called it, escape, and it had been exciting, running off to a new country with her young man, with talk of marriage, great job prospects, a house of their own.

The longer she had been gone, the darker home became in her mind. The city at night – its tight knot of empty office blocks, its locked parks, desolate gapsites where old homes had been torn down and new homes had not yet been built – its only brightness the motorway which shot through the dark heart of it all.

The door of The Amanda is open to the street. The rain is slanting across the doorway like rods of neon. Inside, the bar is dingy, noisy, ugly. The R & B band play flat and raw, beardless boys grinning through songs of death, destruction and state penitentiaries. On the dance floor Joe, ex-jockey from Alabama, is showing Nelly how much better than the youngsters he can jive, his wiry body squirming like a weasel's, his eyes bright with cunning. Nelly looks like she's loving it all.

At the table nearest the dance floor, next to Fiona, sits Tamara. She is shaking her rat tail hair in time to the band. Tamara is very young, serious, scruffy.

I was brought up in an atmosphere of violence, sexual violence, I mean my dad never raised a hand to my mom but it was there, I know it was there. My boyfriend needs to really get inside my sociology for things to work out between us. My singing helps me keep it all altogether and hang loose. I sing blues but no sexist shit, you know. I write my own lyrics about the environment, the trees and the water and the Indians and the whales. And sexual violence, you know there's a lot I have to sing about. I want people to hear these things so maybe I can do some good. Maybe someone out hears what I'm saying. I do these voice exercises so I can sing real low, like a black woman. That's what I really want to do, to sing like a black woman. But I don't dig some black women's blues, I mean the old stuff, Bessie Smith, Billie Holliday, I guess those women were real messed up too. I mean you listen to the lyrics and some of the lyrics are real sexist. I guess they must have sold out to make money. I don't care about money at all. I'll never sell out, not my music. I'm recording my songs when I feel it's the right time, like timing's real important. The moon influences everything we do, I mean look at the tides, look at that huge ocean, the moon influences that huge ocean, so think what it can do to us little people. That's why I like living out west where I can be part of that huge thing, that moontide. The Pacific waves are deep, they influence my music on a real deep level. I'm calling my songs Wise Womanist Blues.

Beneath the bridges of Glasgow, bridges named after trading posts of the old days – Jamaica Bridge, Kingston Bridge, names which as a child spoke to her of sugar and spice, though nowadays reggae music and ganja are more profitable exports – beneath the bridges, the river at night flowed black and viscous as crude oil, with its yellow sheen, the river which had swallowed bodies and hoarded the ghosts of shipyard workers, meths drinkers, wild careless children, desperate mothers, reckless teenagers, bankrupt businessmen, existential students, failed painters, defeated boxers, distracted lovers, pleasure sailors, U.S. Navy personnel, gamblers, debtors, people whose secrets had been found out, people whose secrets were about to be found out, quiet, lonely people who had no secrets and couldn't foresee ever having any. Those who fell and those who were pushed.

Fiona is at the table with friends, new friends, women she has dragged out of their domestic worlds for a night on the town, women who only see each other when Fiona calls round in her beat-up car which she can barely afford to run but runs anyway, so she can do things like this, so she can offer her friends a ride and clatter up the highway twice a month to meet Kent in his mother's cluttered apartment with its lamps which blow fuses every time they use the place and clocks which chime every fifteen minutes, warning that time is moving on willy-nilly and if she doesn't get her act together here, now, between one chime and the next, the past will catch up with the present and the future will be written up as appointments in Kent's diary (under Gym).

She had arranged things with Kent from the beginning. They met while his wife Alice was on a trip to Europe. Kent omitted to mention the existence of Alice until he and Fiona had gone well past being strangers in the night. Not that they had gone much further than meeting for sex – on his mother's bed – his wife's photo in his wallet, and his daughter's.

He brought his toilet bag. She brought food, wine and flowers for the waxed dining table. And bedsheets. In Kent's mother's apartment were trunks full of linen; embroidered pillowcases, bolster rolls, eiderdowns, patchwork quilts, but even though she was unlikely to return from the nursing home, Fiona brought her own bedsheets, which Kent thought bizarre but Fiona knew was simply superstitious. A sinner should not leave traces and screwing a married man, worse, being in love with him, was, in her mind – put there long ago and never rooted out – sinful. And sin – though she would never use the word in any seriousness – brought with it guilt. And guilt, like the ragged insistent chimes of too many clocks, came round again and again.

But you have to have fun once in a while and tonight everyone is really trying hard to do just that. Nobody minds that the band is mediocre or that the place is drab. Nobody seems to notice. It's a change, it's new to them, that's the thing, that's what west coast living is about, being somewhere new, somewhere young. Everyone at the table is from somewhere else, though none as far from home as Fiona.

The big break across the Atlantic had its difficult moments, but the rest was easy, easy once she ceased being Fiona Fell of Maryhill, Glasgow, Scotland and became just another landed immigrant, a drifter. Apart from other expatriate Scots, people she met often didn't know where her country was, far less her city. And after she'd described the weather and the lack of work, most people didn't enquire further, so it was easy to let the old loyalties and irritations peel off, old skin left in the old country. After the initial wrench, loosening her mother's hands from her neck, rubbing the ache where her mother's fingers had clung on until she had to break away, to escape by bus, train, plane from all that was so familiar, it was invisible until those final moments. Invisible and then suddenly and painfully vivid. She'd said she'd be able to save the fare in no time if wages were as good as Donnie had been told.

After the farewell, turning away from her mother's tearful smiles and her father's unsteady handshake, the rest was casual, accidental, easy. There was everything to look forward to and she was impatient to be away, to be with Donnie, who would be waiting in the departure lounge.

"Don't be late," he had joked, "Or I'll go without you." But in the end it was she who had gone on without Donnie.

They were both in the new world still, but now three thousand miles and a $500 round trip ticket apart. When the marriage fell apart – so much water under the bridge now was all she'd say of it – she had pushed on west, a year here, six months there, taking, in all, seven years to cross Canada. Donnie settled into east coast city ways which kept him working long hours to make the rent, blowing out on stimulants every weekend to compensate and never getting around to seeing all those places he'd told Fiona about.

Fiona had seen plenty places, met plenty people. She had addresses all over Canada – a bed or at least a floor for the night if she were to go back east on a visit. It was all there and she had taken part, had joined in wherever she found herself, working at whatever was to hand, joining associations, unions and women's groups, the peace movement. She had reached her destination, the west. There was no doubt it was beautiful and also, as far as accommodation was concerned, this time she had been lucky. Not another crummy apartment but a house, with gleaming hardwood floors and a view; sailboats moored in the bay, ferries ploughing across the straight, tree-covered islands close up and in the distance, glittering snow-capped peaks. But part of her couldn't quite acclimatise to the abundance of everything, the forests so tall and strong, the berry bushes so laden with fruit, the supermarkets shelves piled high with bulk-buy value packs. Part of her remained inert. A hard, dark seam ran through her.

Joe is dancing with Sharon who intently ignores his encouraging winks and jabbing, bony elbows. Nelly has returned to the table, flushed from dancing. She smoothes down her hair with her hands, making it neat – like the rest of her – neat, clean, with the kind of scrubbed look which comes from hours spent outdoors, tending vegetables and fixing up her cheap but decrepit house.

I put one bucket under the real big hole and emptied it each morning until I could borrow my neighbour's ladder to go up and do something temporary about the shingles and then another drip got going in Casey's bedroom so I moved his bed and put the paint tray down to catch the splashes. Then last night when the rain begins again I see two new puckers in the ceiling and I think, Oh my God, the whole house is gonna fall in on me and Casey, we're gonna be drowned in our beds and Ronnie's not due home for a month and there's no money to pay for a new roof anyway until next spring – and I'm wondering how much longer is this rain gonna go on falling, it just seems like it's never gonna stop, it's a flood, a slow dreary flood, seeping in from all sides, tunnelling through the cracks like a plague of worms, rotting the roots of my carrots and beets, eating away my home. But I love the summer here, I really love the summer and I guess we need some of this rain. At least we don't have the cold they get back east. Deep down I'm a pioneer at heart and a pioneer's gotta put up with some tough times. My grandparents had it real tough when they came to Canada from Holland. Dirt poor, they were. Dropped off on the Prairies with a logpile and told to get building a house for themselves before winter came and snowed them under. They had everything to learn. My grandfather was a postman back home and my grandmother was a seamstress – what did they know about housebuilding? But between them they knocked up a shack for themselves and it gave them shelter from the snow which that winter banked up around them to the rafters. Deep down I just love it here on the island. Even the rain can be kind of neat, I mean, I get the stove going and pull in the sofa and sit all evening drinking tea and reading long novels. Trilogies are my favourite. It's so neat to meet up with a character in a new setting, it's just like coming out tonight and meeting everybody again. Oh my God, it's so good to get out. And I just love this band.

Nelly, Tamara, Sharon, Fiona. Apart from Fiona, they lived with men, for better or worse. Fiona knew that none of them was ecstatic about their life, having spent many an hour in her apartment – a popular refuge for Nelly, Tamara and Sharon – listening late into the night to the troubles of her friends, offering advice and tea. It was good to feel useful, good to feel part of others' lives but it wasn't enough. And the situation with Kent was hopeless. She was cut off from any normal access, obliged to be a woman in waiting. It wasn't enough any more. There had been times when it might have been, when life was light and men were disposable but now when she looked forward, the future looked lonely. No children, no work – she hadn't counted on unemployment here – and no man. It wasn't enough.

Sharon returns to the table by herself. Joe meanders back towards the table but instead of sitting down, continues on to the bar, patting Fiona's back as he passes, letting her know with a nudge and a shoulder squeeze that he hasn't forgotten her, the first woman at the table to speak to him, the one responsible for his array of dancing partners.

That guy! says Sharon. *It's hard to believe he and Brad are the same species. Know what he said to me? 'I must be the luckiest guy in the room to have all you ladies at my table.' I mean, he joined us. And nobody invited him. 'All you ladies.' Does he think he's going to take us all home with him? But I mean, I just can't imagine Brad ever in his life coming out with such dumb lines. Or Nelly's Ronnie. Or even Tamara's Crazy Dave. Or Kent. Been seeing him at all? It must be tough him being so unavailable but really, a man can be too available. It's important to be on your own. If I don't find time in the day for myself, just to sit down in my home, alone, I get stressed, know what I mean? I start to feel this ache up around the back of my neck and my head goes kind of stiff and my jaw starts to hurt and I feel like my lips are drawn tight across my face, exposing my teeth, that I'm like a trapped animal, all tied up inside, ready to spring. That's when Brad and the kids know they'd better get the hell out of the house. But usually it doesn't come to that because deep down we get along pretty well. We're family. It must be a whole lot different for you. I heard – but maybe you know already – that Kent and Alice aren't getting along. They're sleeping apart, which says something. Do you reckon he'll leave her? But maybe you wouldn't want that, you've got your own life, keep yourself busy, know so many people, do so many things. I wish I had the time for activities but with the job and Brad and the kids, the days seem to fill up so fast. You can do so much more if you're independent. When Brad and I are fighting I really think I'd like to be alone again. But then I meet a guy like Joe and I'm thankful I'm not.*

Now it is Fiona's turn to push through the cluster of wet-eyed drunks, swaying and sweating at the edge of the dance floor, heads jerking like puppets in time to the music. Joe is close up behind her, pushing her through the crowd with his skinny fingers, rubbing up against her with his narrow thighs, his jeans dragging against her skirt with a crackle of static.

They reach the dance floor. Fiona turns to him and begins to speak. He can't hear what she's saying because of the music so she cups her hand over his ear and repeats,

"I think I'll pass on this dance." Joe mimes his disappointment. It is comical, exaggerated, false but still he takes her arm and attempts to lead her on to the floor.

"Tamara likes to dance," says Fiona but he still can't hear her, so she breaks away, arcs her palm across her face in a brisk, farewell wave and weaves through the dancers to the street door. Outside, she turns down one side street and another, glancing back to make sure that Joe hasn't followed her, cuts back to where her car is parked, climbs in and drives off along the streets, wet and black as rivers, towards the beckoning fountain of light at the highway intersection, with no direction in mind which feels like home.

Lesley Smith

SHORTS

good homes wanted by

shy sheep
calm companionable cow
and porky pig pal.

*

trying to get the toys out of the attic
opening the oven door and stepping inside.

retreating to the echo of blankets.

*

suffocated by a wish.

*

the most unforgettable strawberry jam
explores something within you

*

Maud Sulter

NO OXBRIDGE SPIRES

Do you remember how a grocers shop used to be? My granddad was a grocer y'know. Didn't own his own shop, it was part of a chain but he did the books and ordered the stock. Worked until he was seventy-two y'know.

We used to live three stairs up in a tenement. A one room and kitchen. There was a large Belfast sink that I used to be bathed in. It seemed enormous as I was very small. The coal fire in the kitchen was the fulcrum of the household. We would sit around it on the red vinyl three piece suite and chat, play games or even watch the television. Viewing was more by choice then rather than compulsion. The lobby had the coal bunker in and whenever I passed it I would be terrified that someone would jump out at me as I went through to the big room. That was where my granddad slept in the box bed behind a curtain. There was a fireplace in there too and another suite but we never seemed to spend much time in there. It also had an enormous bay window with a trio of sash frames. I would often spend hours hanging out of the middle one with the view of the street's length and right into the park, observing the comings and goings. These days it would be called being nosey but then it served as street policing. Everyone knew what everyone was up to so it was less likely that anyone would get away with a scam.

Sometimes, after my granddad retired, his bad leg got the better of him, and I was able to walk, we would take a trip out to one of the grocers shops where he spent his working days. His eyes were bad so he never went to fight in the wars but I always remember a story about his brother who came back from the Somme with his puttees stuck to his flesh. The caked mud would have taken his skin clean off the bone if my granny hadn't kept soaking his feet and legs up to the knees in the tin bath. 'There was mair life in that uniform,' she would say, 'than they brought back from that battle.'

I never knew my grandmother on my mother's side. She died

112

a long time before I was born. We only have one photograph of her. She looks very old and very grey but apparently was less than forty when the image was taken. Sometimes that fixed image makes me feel frustrated. I'm sure that I would have a more rounded picture of her in my mind's eye if I did not have that ghostly resemblance on a photographic plane.

Anyway, those trips to the grocers were a real event. I would inevitably want to take my pram and my dollies, which I'd get fed up pushing after half a block. On the one hand this would be a relief to the citizens of the area as I was a terror with it running into peoples ankles. On the other hand it meant that my granddad, who was not a short man, had to push it eighteen inches off the ground.

I've never been able to push a pram straight which is probably something to do with the fact that once I was able to fly. Well of course it's a well known fact that black people could fly before slavery days and that our wings are reforming to this very day but the incident which I am here recounting was rather more perambulatory. There I was in my pram only a few months old. As I was four pounds at birth I don't reckon that I weighed more than a half dozen bags of sugar at the time. Anyway, it was a windy day and my mum and my auntie wanted to go to a drapers shop along at Crown Street in the Gorbals. Well as I said it was windy and my granddad said, 'Don't you be taking my precious,' that's what he called me, 'Don't you be taking my precious out in that weather.' Well, my mum and my auntie persisted, so there we all were setting out on 'The Curtain Mission' with my big cousin Linda, or was it Yvonne, who was only six at the time.

Well, you wouldn't think that between them my mum and my auntie had brought up four children because weren't they daft enought to put up the hood so that I wouldn't be in a draft. So there we were half way along Caledonia Road when Whoosh! Off I fly like the ancestors on my daddy's side. Over the railings, into the park, which dear reader I feel obliged to point out was only yards from the Clyde. My mum rushed into the park and found me still strapped in and, so the story goes, smiling sweetly. My auntie on the other hand had to go to hospital to get stitches because she held onto the pram when it took flight and was impaled on the railings and my cousin lost a couple of milkteeth. Still, we've all dined out many times on this adventure, each rendering our own version of the tale of course.

As I was saying, when my granddad and I would visit these grocers it would always be an event. The staff in the shops would always make as much fuss of him as me. So while they gossiped and reminisced I would explore the three feet high sacks and tubs of pulses and flour, rice and other grains, which would lead the way in from the main door. The dark wood panelling of the shops would be polished so that you could see your face in it and the brasses shone as if of solid gold. From a huge mound of opaque butter the wooden pats would shape a half-pound which would then be wrapped in grease proof paper and placed in a paper bag for us to take home to have on oatcakes with cheese for a snack. We would listen to *Whistle While You Work* on the radio with an air of superiority as we had already done all of our housework well before and would wait for my mum coming home from working on the buses if she was on an early shift. I often think the reason I don't like the colour green is the fact that for the entire period of my gestation I was encased in a bottlegreen Corporation uniform skirt.

I worked as a clippie until the day I was born and then, as if that wasn't endeavour enough, had to sleep in the bottom drawer from the big wardrobe until a cot was bought. The cot was of course splendidly magnificent but it just goes to show that it isn't all roses being a firstborn.

Yesterday I went to buy some lambs' liver in the local butchers. His computerised scales had packed it in so he had to judge the weight and price by his hands and in his head. He seemed more human than usual, he even made some conversation. And it made me wonder about how communities are lost. No Oxbridge spires for us. No ancient relics carved in stone. No permanence. My granddad was a grocer y'know. Didn't own his own shop. Worked until he was seventy-two y'know.

Anne Tall

DREAM-SONGS FOR WINTERS

the clearance

That night
I dreamed between
red sheets of flame

Children called to me
from their milky sleep
We pulled two boys
from the white throat of the river

We saved what we could
whatever we could carry outside
into the snow
We heard only echoes
of the foreign voices that raised
that fire around us

Behind them
our houses burned down into darkness

No food. No shelter.
There was no love left for us anywhere

After that night
the names, the stories
were locked in our own old barbarous tongue

After that winter
we disappeared
into the soft grey mouths of the stones.

2   *the coast*

We clung to those cliffs like sea-birds
Already,
I had dreamed my blue-green death
my drab plunge from that crumbling edge
heart shrunk to a knot
womb to a stone

The nets and boats they'd given us
had rotted before we came
Our seeds were blown to the sea's mouth
or shrivelled from damp and sand
All winter
we exchanged what we could for potatoes

The men learned the stars
that plot out the sea's curve
its tides, its roars and whispers
The women
how to gut and bone that one poor harvest
the small trapped lives
that gasped and died

Not even our songs had roots there
Up out of the past
they sprang from our tongue, full and green
with one story only
The future was somewhere else
And in another language

3   *the prairie*

No waves sound here
though the prairie was a sea voyage
on a calm day

At first
my tongue refused those hard flat vowels
their speech was like tin
no-one could sing in that language
My presence here was a silence
blank and still

Closed in by weather and distance
Cut off by words
women attend the births and deaths of babies
Men dream money and land (only they can own)
And this country opening up to them
brimming with children, lakes, mountains and cities
All bearing the names they have given them

At the edge
of what has been cleared
the wilderness persists

All day it presses in on me
Snake, Bear, Wolf, Owl, something watches me
In the dark, terrified, I wait
for the hot rank breath on my neck
Feathers rustle beneath my skin
Fur glistens along my back
Claws, beaks tear open the delicate features
Entered and transformed I win back old territory
In the morning
the cabin, the path and the clearing say
It was only a dream

Men leave land to their sons
My daughter will inherit the stove, the churn and the wash-tub
And in my own tongue, the songs and stories
Small charms against the silence and the distances
And those times at night
when a man spurts another mouth into her
And she cries out, calling
for the wolves to finish it

WINTER TREE

Cold earth, cold roots
sharp angles and thorns
a hoarder
of shadows, empty of songs

Bone naked
it seems the dark shape of a woman
rising there
    wildhaired, poised
as though she'd danced
then froze
in a blast of wintry air

Winter thin
those stiff limbs where
leaf and blossom sleep unseen,
rain's music unplayed,
whole forests undreamed
    While the moon
places there
a clear glass   night-edged
mirror   to my season

NOT VIRGINIA WOOLF

a few hours
hoarded
like coins from the housekeeping
a few hours
set aside
from housework and the care of children
from the endless tugs of love and routine
a few hours
saved
to spend on some extravagance
like a story, a painting, a poem

a room of her own?

time
would be enough
time
and silence

Afterword

Original Prints III has been a long time in the making. Between our requests for new writing from Scottish women in the winter of 1987 and this volume's appearance in the summer of 1989 Polygon has moved, lock and stock, from being a part of Edinburgh University Student Publications to operating as an imprint of Edinburgh University Press.

The editorial continuity of Original Prints suffered a bit from the changeover. At some point during the flit from old Polygon to new, a large bundle of submissions and correspondence went missing. On behalf of everybody at Polygon we would like to apologise to any women still wondering what has happened to their stories, poems or letters. Also several women seem to have moved house during the interim. If they want to write to us, we will send on their submissions now.

We are hoping that an Original Prints IV will appear towards the beginning of 1991, and will accept contributions between January 1 and April 31 1990. Any women keen to commit themselves to being on the editorial group for this project are invited to contact us at the address below.

Marion Sinclair and Jenny Turner
Original Prints
Polygon
22 George Square
Edinburgh EH8 9LF

Contributors

VIVIEN ADAM was born in Huntly, Aberdeenshire, in 1958. She studied English and Philosophy at Aberdeen Uni, where she was part of a performing poetry group, and worked in Camphill communities in Aberdeen and Dumfries. For the last year she has been working as Administrator at the new Buckhaven St Andrews Theatre in Fife, where her first original play, *Jonah and the Jaws of Death*, was performed last November.

TERESA ANDERSON was born and raised in Durham. She now lives in Edinburgh where she is doing research into small-scale hydropower in the Department of Electrical Engineering at Edinburgh University. This is her first appearance in print.

SHEENA BLACKHALL is the single parent of four children, on Income Support. Three volumes of her poetry, *The Cyard's Kist*, *The Spik O' The Lan* and *Hamedrauchtit*, have been published by Rainbow Enterprises, who are due to bring out a fourth collection, *The Nor' East Neuk*, shortly. *A Nippick o Nor' East Tales* was published in January 1989 by Keith Murray Publications, who are also publishing a new poetry collection, *Fite Dool/Black Crow* in June. She recently won the Robert McLellan Silver Tassie for her story 'Reets' and has had work published in *Edinburgh Review*, *Cencrastus*, *Lallans* and *The Leopard* among other Scots magazines. She is a full time poet, writer and illustrator.

ELIZABETH BURNS lives in Edinburgh, where she works with the women's publishing group Stramullion. She has had poetry published in various magazines, and in *Original Prints II*.

SUSAN CHANEY was born near Cambridge in 1957, but spent most of her childhood in a small village near Cornwall.

121

She has lived in Edinburgh for the past 15 years and has three children, two of whom are twins. She is presently taking a diploma in Community Education at Edinburgh University and has been writing for three years.

MAUD DEVINE: Born Glasgow, 1948. Former teacher turned misoweanist. Now Mobile Librarian going round in circles and hoping for a transfer to Hawaii. Has published work with *The Glasgow Herald,* The Third Eye Centre, *New Writing Scotland* 4 and *The West Coast Magazine.*

ANNE DOWNIE is a graduate of Glasgow University and RSAMD. She is a professional actress and playwright who has lately branched out into solo comedy, appearing in Channel 4's 'Halfway to Paradise'. She has had ten plays professionally produced, including 'Waiting on One' for Wildcat (winner of LWT's £10,000 prize) and her stage adaptation of Kesson's novel *The White Bird Passes.* Her next play, based on *The Yellow on the Broom* will tour from February 89. Her story 'Walter' appeared in *Original Prints I.* Two of her plays are published. She is a Glaswegian, married with two children.

GERRIE FELLOWS has lived in three countries, all reputed to speak the same language. Her poetry, which has a Southern English accent, has appeared in *Writing Women, Cencrastus, Edinburgh Review* and *Variant,* and has been recorded for STV's *In Verse* series. She lives in Glasgow.

JANICE GALLOWAY was born in Ayrshire where she still teaches (though now part time, thanks to the help of good friends). She now lives in Glasgow. Her stories have appeared in *Edinburgh Review, Radical Scotland, Chapman, Margin, West Coast Magazine, Aurora, The Glasgow Herald* and in anthologies from Polygon, The Women's Press, Serpent's Tail and Sheba. Her first novel is due out next year, but she's still coming to terms with the fact that writers have nae money.

THELMA GOOD was born and grew up in Edinburgh and lives on the edge of the city in the village of Juniper Green. She has a philosophy degree from Dundee University. She performs her poetry in Edinburgh and other places in Britain.

ANNE HAY was born in Perth and studied French at St Andrews University. She now lives in Edinburgh with her husband and two children. She won second prize in the Edinburgh International Writers' Weekend New Writing Competition in 1987, and has recently been involved with the Perserverance Writers' Club in publishing their own book of short stories.

A.L. KENNEDY was born in Dundee but now lives in Glasgow and works in Clydebank. Her short stories have appeared in magazines, including *Stand* and *Bête Noir*, and will be included in the anthologies *The Devil and the Giro* and *Behind the Lines*. An only child, she lives alone.

LINDA McCANN runs a workshop of women writers in Maryhill, Glasgow and is currently putting together an anthology of its work. She also works as an Adult Education tutor and edits the youth section of a local newspaper.

RUTH McILROY was born in 1956 in Wales, one of five sisters. She spent her early childhood in Jamaica and was educated in Edinburgh where she now lives. She mainly writes poems, which have been published in various places; this is her first real venture into prose.

ROSEMARY MACKAY comes from Aberdeen. She is a part-time tutor with the W.E.A. and has recently published *Models* with Keith Murray Publications.

LINDSAY McKRELL was brought up in Stirling and Dunblane and studied French and Russian at Heriot-Watt University. She has been an active member of Leith Writers' Workshop and has poems published in *Original Prints II*. After graduating this summer she spent five months in Brussels working for the Socialist Group in the European Parliament, and is now 'positively unemployed' in Stirling.

MAUREEN MacNAUGHTAN comes from Glasgow but is at present in her first year at Aberdeen University. Her poems have been printed in magazines including *Voices Israel, Poetry Review, Iron, Poets for Africa USA, New Writing Scotland, Gallimaufry*, and in the English small press.

ANGELA McSEVENEY was born in 1964 and has lived in Ross-shire, Livingston and the Borders before moving to Edinburgh in 1982 to be a student. She has published poems with various magazines and in *Original Prints II*. Her 'unemployment' poems came about during a six month period of joblessness in 1986 and 1987; she presently works as a Library Assistant in Edinburgh.

JANET PAISLEY lives near Falkirk, a single parent with six sons. She has published countless short stories under various pseudonyms and her stories and poems have won prizes in many competitions including the Poetry Society National Open poetry competition and the Swanage Literary Competition. Public readings include appearances at Mayfest, the Edinburgh, Stirling and Falkirk Festivals and several poetry broadcasts for radio and TV. Her poetry is collected in *Pegasus in Flight* (Rookbook Publications, Edinburgh) and *Images*, poetry on video (ETV/AV Services, Moray House). A second poetry video from Moray House is due out in June 1989.

JOY PITMAN was born in Bristol in 1945, moved to Scotland in 1973, has worked as a teacher, archivist, mother, publisher and administrator, and is currently training in psychotherapy. Her poems have been published by Stramullion, Polygon and several Scottish magazines.

124

DILYS ROSE is presently in western Canada but normally lives in Edinburgh. A first collection of poems (Chapman Publications) and a first collection of short stories (Secker & Warburg) are due to appear in autumn 1989.

LESLEY SMITH was born in Glasgow and lives in Renfrew. She is a student at Glasgow School of Art, studying Printed Textiles.

MAUD SULTER was born and brought up in Glasgow. *As a Blackwoman*, her first collection of poetry, was published by Akira Press in 1985. A journalist and visual artist, she is currently completing her M.A. in photographic studies, in which her special field is rememory.

ANNE TALL lives in Glasgow with her daughter, which she likes, but has no contact with other women writers, which she doesn't.